"This book is so great
over and get something
dant with spiritual wisd   ...ank you."

—A woman in OA, New Jersey

"Meredith has written a genuinely honest and Christ-focused guide to accompany your spiritual journey. This book gives you strength and the tools to look at your own life while giving you inspiration. This is a heartfelt tribute to life and God."

—Cheron Price, Niles, Michigan

"As a therapist and overcomer of disordered eating, I'm thrilled with Meredith's holistic and biblical approach to get to the root of food, weight, and addiction. The verses that were critical to me as a young adult overcoming anorexia and bulimia are the same ones used in this guide. God's word is powerful to change our hearts, minds, and bodies, in addition to mental health and medical interventions!"

—Brenda Yoder, Licensed Mental Health Counselor, speaker, author, life coach, author of *Fle♦ge: Launch your Ki♦s Without Losing Your Min♦*, Shipshewana, IN

"Meredith's story speaks to the power of faith and living in the solution. She should know. As Meredith's journey takes the reader into a succession of failed attempts to find a way out of her personal purgatory, she dispels the myth of diets, weight loss, alcohol, and relationships offering our 'salvation.' Meredith is clear the solution rests in our ability to cultivate a spiritual lifestyle that allows us to take advantage of the rich resources provided to us when we put faith in the front of the line."

—Mary Lerner, PhD, CEO, Milestones in Recovery Treatment Center, Cooper City, FL

"This is the story of one woman's personal recovery from food addiction using Christian biblical spirituality and the 12-step program. With many references to Christian Scriptures, Meredith shares the powerful and honest testimony of her process for those who want to recover with Jesus."

—Theresa Wright, MS, RD, LDN, Owner, Renaissance in Nutrition, Norristown, PA

"This guide was awesome to read. I have been in the 12-step rooms for years. What I needed to hear were the Scriptures you put into the guide. It showed me the perfect peace that Jesus, God, and Holy Spirit give me. I use the steps as a guide to live. I use the Bible and Scriptures to hear how God is talking to me. The guide helped me grow spiritually and to fall into the arms of my loving creator."

—Jacqui, OA/AA

"Being a mental health professional who studies the relationship of childhood trauma and obesity, I 'get it.' But Meredith takes this book and makes it so that even those of us who think we 'get it' have to revisit our own relationships with food. I highly recommend this book for anyone struggling to understand their food battles. It is a huge blessing for everyone!"

—Marla Godette, MA, Founding Mentor, Mentoring Moments, LLC, South Bend, IN

"Meredith gives 'Healthy Voice' encouragement and great weight-loss advice along with her honesty and openness to share her personal story and experiences, a place that unlocks pieces of our own wounded hearts. She reminds us along the way that God is so near and willing to meet us in our deepest hurts, 'He knows we have baggage, and it doesn't scare Him. It may scare us, but it doesn't scare Him.' With each chapter she points us to God's Scriptures and Holy Spirit–inspired prayers shining light on our dark rejections, shame, guilt, self-doubt, leading us to be all that God has called us to be."

—Lori Shepler, Light on the Hill Outreach Church, Donegal, PA

How to Let Go

OF YOUR FOOD
AND WEIGHT OBSESSION

A guide for the woman who
wants more for her life

MEREDITH TERPELUK SCHOELLER

BROOKSTONE
PUBLISHING GROUP
Birmingham, Alabama

How to Let Go of Your Food and Weight Obsession

Brookstone Publishing Group
An imprint of Iron Stream Media
100 Missionary Ridge
Birmingham, AL 35242
IronStreamMedia.com

Copyright © 2022 by Meredith Terpeluk Schoeller

Library of Congress Control Number is available.

Cover design by Hannah Linder Designs

ISBN: 978-1-949856-65-1 (paperback)
ISBN: 978-1-949856-66-8 (e-book)

1 2 3 4 5—26 25 24 23 22

This book is dedicated to every woman who has ever struggled with her food or weight, especially those of the next generation who currently battle eating disorders and food addiction. May this guide help you break the cycle.

CONTENTS

✕ Part I: Changing Your Mindset ✕

✕ Part II: Turning Over the Food and Weight to God ✕

✕ Part III: Dealing with Your Heart Wounds ✕

✕ Part IV: Making Recovery a Lifestyle ✕

Preface

Have I not commanded you? Be strong and courageous. Do not be afraid; do not be discouraged, for the LORD your God will be with you wherever you go.

—Joshua 1:9

Hi, my name is Meredith, and I want to tell you a little about why I wanted to write this book. When I was finishing up my first round of writing, my daughter Elianah was just weeks away from turning two. She was in that phase of toddlerhood where she loved pointing out invisible "ouchies" on her legs so Mommy could kiss them.

We would then put multiple cool Band-Aids on her legs, even in places where there were no ouchies because that's just what you do. Whether you are a mom or not, you've probably heard something about how quickly little kids heal. What's funny about that is that the older we get as adults, the harder it is for our wounds to heal, especially those deeper wounds no one can see.

Unlike the outside ones that become scars, you can't tell if the inside ones have healed. Because of that, we often try to do what the world tells us—improve the outside—with Band-Aids like diets or overeating. Then we wonder why neither does the trick. That is the space I'm meeting you in with this book, my friend—where you know there is something more to this and you just can't put your finger on it. I want to help you with that.

There is a space beyond what you've thought, where you no longer have to use those surface Band-Aids to heal those heart wounds. In that space is God, and He wants to be your healer this time. He wants to take over where you are so used to beating yourself up for faulty willpower.

Many of us have emotional baggage around our food and weight. So many things in life cause us to cope with overeating or turning right to the diet. But I believe God wants to do something new. He says,

> *See, I am ₁oing a new thing!*
>   *Now it springs up; ₁o you not perceive it?*
> *I am making a way in the wil₁erness*
>   *an₁ streams in the wastelan₁.* (Isaiah 43:19)

He wants you to overcome this struggle with His help so you can actually have lasting victory over it. But He is not the God of the "quick fix."

In this guide you will hear me reference two things: Scripture and 12-step recovery because they are the things that have worked for me. Just like I had to learn, you will be the one responsible for yourself and taking action where you see fit. I certainly don't expect you to do it the same way I did because we are all different. But my hope is that you will see the value in what has worked for me and countless others. Then, go from there.

Before we go any further, I want to suggest three things for you to get to go along with this. Some of you may already have them. First, get yourself a Bible if you don't have one. There are multiple translations, but if it's your first time, I suggest the New International Version (NIV) or even *The Message*. Believe me, this is the greatest road map for life you could ever have.

Second—and I know this may sound scary, but—get yourself a copy of *The Big Book of Alcoholics Anonymous*. You can order it online and no one will ever see. I am telling you, it will help you understand yourself better and your attachment to food and weight. Yes, alcoholic may be in the title but try not to get caught up in that. This book has helped millions of people break all kinds of addictions. I know the first time I picked it up, I immediately thought of my relationship with food, and I am certainly not alone in that. Give it a chance.

Third, get a journal. You will need it to process what you learn about yourself here. If you are in a group as you read this, it will be even better because it will help you work through the emotions and thoughts that will come up on the journey together. I don't care if you aren't a writer, or you've never picked up the journal you actually bought months ago. I just care that you use it. Write down insights, inspiration, and Scripture—whatever you need to grow—it will be an important tool for you.

What I share here is the testament to what God has done in my life, and I share it primarily because (1) I want to give Him glory, and (2) I believe He wants to help you too. I don't want one drop of this to be about what I did, but what God has done and continues to do for me. It's also not about the weight I've lost or before-and-after pictures. It's about His work in my life when I didn't focus on all that. To God be the glory.

I pray God works in your life through this guide. I pray whatever He does for you and in you that you pass it on and give Him all the glory. Author and pastor Rick Warren wrote, "Other people are going to find healing in your wounds. Your greatest life messages and your most effective ministry will come out of your deepest hurts."[1]

I hope by my sharing what the Lord did in my life, you will find it's important to do the same for the people in your life. This journey has absolutely been one of the longest, deepest, and hardest battles of my life. I have no doubt it has been somewhat similar for you. Just know you aren't alone.

At the end of each chapter, you will find a prayer. Whereas some authors would have this be a prompting for personal prayer, these are blessings I've been praying over you while writing this book. If you are unfamiliar with prayer in the spirit or intimidated by prayer in general, it will help guide you. If you already pray in the Spirit, I pray this is an addition to the prayer I'm sure you already do.

Father, I pray you will use my wor•s to bring you glory an• reach the hearts of those who want to receive your goo•ness. May your Wor• bring hope an• healing an• give this rea•er a •esire to pursue you more. Thank you, Lor•, for everything you have •one to get me on the recovery journey an• for getting this person to pick up this book. Lor•, I ask that in this process, you free them from the shackles of surface fixes an• heal their heart woun•s as only you can. In your name, I pray. Amen.

Introduction

I want to tell you why this book is more about letting go of the food and weight obsession than about repairing the surface. The simple fact is that you are special to God. Your life and who He created you to be is worth way more to Him than to be constantly focused on food and weight. You can doubt me, but just think for a minute how much you've thought about "solving" these things over the years. Now let this statement start to sink in:

This has always been about your heart, not the food or weight; and the only one who can fix it is God.

Yes, that means not you, not me, not the diet, or the food you like best. If you don't know it yet, you need to know it now:

God is not looking at your body. He's looking at your heart.

But the LORD sai◆ to Samuel, "Do not consi◆er his appearance or his height, for I have rejecte◆ him. The LORD ◆oes not look at things people look at. People look at the outwar◆ appearance, but the LORD looks at the heart." (1 Samuel 16:7)

Saying "I look fat" to yourself in the mirror, or "Do I look fat?" to your friend or spouse, or constantly worrying about how to lose the weight is a waste of time. The one whose opinion is above any other is more interested in what's going on with your heart than what number is on the scale. It's your faith, not that number, that will transform you.

I have no doubt that many of you reading this have at least a mustard seed of faith. If you don't, that's fine. I'm glad you are here, and I pray this book plants a seed. Some of you may be longtime Christ-followers. For some of you, maybe a seed was planted long ago that you stopped watering and you are interested in nurturing the soil again. Whatever the case, I'm willing to bet you have prayed for God to remove either the weight or your food obsession. "Just make it go away, Lord!" Maybe you've gotten to the point when it doesn't go away so you start to think maybe God isn't there or prayers don't work. That's a lie. The truth is God has always known you have the problem. You've just been looking in the wrong direction because while you've been busy all these years begging Him to take it away or trying to do it without Him, He's just been waiting for you to hear what He's trying to tell you.

Look at the apostle Paul in 2 Corinthians 12. He begs God three times to remove the thorn from his side. We don't know what that thorn is but imagine it's an unhealthy behavior or vice. Verses 9 and 10 say, *"But he said to me, 'My grace is sufficient for you, for my power is made perfect in weakness.' Therefore, I will boast all the more gladly about my weaknesses, so that Christ's power may rest on me. That is why, for Christ's sake, I delight in weaknesses, in insults, in hardships, in persecutions, in difficulties. For when I am weak, then I am strong."*

Did you catch that? The Lord told Paul that His grace was sufficient for him because His power is made perfect in weakness. It's like a permission slip that says, "You don't have to do this alone!" In the course of this chapter, Paul realizes it's about giving God the glory in his weakness because that's what makes him strong. The Lord is not saying, "Go heal your weakness yourself and then I'll approve of you." He's saying, "I already know you have this problem. I can be your strength, so will you just let me help you?" Can you relate to that?

I sure can. I don't know about you, but I've done the whole "fix" food and weight countless times. Today I get exhausted just thinking about it.

I don't know the lengths or depths you've gone to get that food or weight "fix." But I'm betting if we were sitting face-to-face right now, we'd be laughing over our common war stories. It's crazy the lengths we've gone to for the "fix." We think normal eating or normal weight is something to achieve. I've come to believe that's overrated and boring. God's not calling you to be "normal" or like everybody else. You were born to stand apart from the crowd with Him. That's why He's calling you to seek Him instead of the food or weight "fix."

You will seek me and find me when you seek me with all your heart.

—Jeremiah 29:13

If you seek God, since He already knows what's going on, then maybe you can get honest about where you are. Maybe you can admit that this relationship with food and weight has blocked you from His voice and you want His guidance to do something different. Maybe it's time to put down that stick you've been using to beat yourself up and let Him work.

Let me tell you a little about when I was ready to put down that stick myself. It was May of 2013. I was in the middle of pursuing a business graduate degree, escaping stress with food and alcohol, and burning off those calories by training for races. One weekend I was doing a race called the Holy Half Marathon on Notre Dame's campus. I was scheduled to attend a wedding that night for a friend from Notre Dame who was a year younger than me. She was getting married in the Basilica, which is a gorgeous church right on campus. It's like the dream wedding venue for alumni. There I was at thirty-one sitting in the back of the church, looking at all her friends who had husbands and kids, wondering what I'd been doing with my life. I was comparing like crazy. The jealousy was evident, and I was beating myself up about everything (including my weight). It didn't matter what my resume looked like at the moment. It mattered that I felt terrible enough about myself that I knew it was time to change.

The next day I found myself crying out to Jesus on my knees in my apartment. The Lord heard my cry.

> *I love the LORD, for he hear♦ my voice;*
>> *he hear♦ my cry for mercy.*
> *Because he turne♦ his ear to me,*
>> *I will call on him as long as I live.* (Psalm 116:1–2)

I can't tell you exactly what He said, but I can tell you it spoke right to my heart. That's how I knew it was Him. It was something like, "Meredith. I'm here for you. I've always been here for you because I love you. I forgive you for whatever you've done you're ashamed of, and I want to help you take the next steps." It was the most comforting moment of my life.

That moment gave me the courage to make some other calls I had to make over the course of a few days. The first person was someone I knew would "get it," whom I knew was already in recovery and would not judge me for admitting that I had the problem.

The second was to my father which was hard because I had to be honest with him in a way I never had (and we were close). He knew I struggled with my weight, but he always thought it was a surface issue too. He was surprised when I said, "Dad, I need help, like *real* help." I remember him saying, "What do you mean, Meredith? You are the most put-together person I know." That's when I realized I wasn't showing up on the outside as who I really was on the inside. I said, "Yeah, but Dad, I'm falling apart on the inside."

I thank God for giving me a father who had seen recovery from addiction in his life.

The third person was the head of the treatment center I'd eventually attend. I can't even express in words the mental and emotional weight I was carrying in my heart when I started talking to him. Filled with shame, regret, self-hatred—I just wanted someone to take it all away, and I was willing to do anything to get better.

Some people in recovery say, "I was just sick and tired of being sick and tired." Maybe you think it hasn't gotten that bad for you. If so, I'm glad. If it has, that is OK. You are right where you need to be. But be careful of the "I'm not that bad" sayings. Once you start comparing what's bad for you to someone else's bad, you may be counting yourself out of getting better. That's why we often say, "Try not to compare." Only you know where you are emotionally, which you can't compare on the surface. When God humbles us, (especially in an area of our life where we thought we had it together), it's a pretty powerful thing because it makes us realize how desperately we need Him. Good thing He meets us right where we are.

The road ahead will look different for each of you. For me, I started by going to treatment and finding the 12 steps of Alcoholics Anonymous. That's what led me to eventually become a Christ follower. Remember, we are all responsible for ourselves, so however the road ahead looks for you is just how it's supposed to be. Maybe for you, it will be just reaching out to a friend and being more honest. Maybe it will be going to a meeting. Maybe it will be working through the rest of this book in a group of fellow believers at your church. I don't know what it will look like. I just pray God remains the center of it all.

It's also important to know in the beginning that the hope we find here is not in any kind of behavior modification program. Our hope is in the Lord. I believe Christine Caine, author of multiple books and Bible studies, evangelist and cofounder of the A21

Campaign to combat human trafficking, said it best, "Christianity is not about behavior modification but heart transformation."

This is serious work that requires the support of our sisters.

That being said, let's get right to the heart of this. Let's talk about the excuses that block us a little bit. (You may want to get out that journal.)

Can you remember the first time you really went to the food, the sugar, the diet, or even the workout for a "fix"? I can remember mine vividly and shared about it in my first book, *Healthy Voice: Life Beyon• the Weight*, which I published in 2012 when I was four years sober. My cousin reminded me of the story in my first few days of treatment. I was seven, and we were at the Jersey Shore in her grandmother's kitchen. There was a breakfast Danish on the table that we wanted to open, but we were told it was off-limits. As we pondered slicing into it, apparently I said to her, "If anyone deserves this it's me because my parents are going through a divorce." Looking back, I know today I had no idea how big that event was or how hard it was to process.

I used it as an excuse for years to keep making unhealthy choices, not just around food but also alcohol. I'd say, "If you knew what I've been through" (when people had been through much worse things). Many of us have been through seriously tough things. That's why it's important to bring them into the light, so we don't have to hold onto the excuses that make us avoid dealing with them.

Also, have you ever blamed God for not being there in the food thing? I have. It felt like He was "up there, not down here" a lot of the time. I truly did ask God multiple times in church on Sundays as a kid, "Why do you hate me so much? You made my parents divorce and you made me overweight. What did I do to you?" His absence (or what felt like it) was another excuse to over-eat. Yet, He had never left.

How about the diets? Have the diets ever been an excuse for you to overeat? I think I was eight when I started dieting. It was right after my parents' divorce because I remember the weight started to pack on. I don't even remember the number on the scale. What I do remember is my eighth-grade graduation dress being a really big size and feeling embarrassed by that. I judged myself so harshly by a number on my clothes when I was just hurting on the inside. Of course that summer before freshman year, I dropped a bunch of weight so I could show off on the first day of school.

Did that change me on the inside? No. Eventually the weight came back on because I started to give myself permission to over-eat, and the cycle just went around over and over again for years of never getting to the root of my pain. Can you relate?

There is something important I want you to know right now.

Your obsession with food and weight has been a tactic of the Enemy to keep you from focusing on God. We will talk more about this later. But I mention it now to start strengthening you with God's help because the Enemy has been working hard for most of your life against you (as he often likes to do). His plan has been to hold you back, keep your thinking defeated, distracted, and weak so you never realize the possibility, power, and presence of God in your life.

Don't underestimate him. He starts earlier. During that experience I just shared from the Jersey Shore, I was seven and I have no doubt he started infiltrating long before that. Start becoming aware of his tactics in your life. It's funny because you've probably been one of those people (like many of us) who had this image of God up in heaven standing next to a scale with a clipboard in His hand, ready to check your weight so He could tell you whether you were worthy of His love. Yeah—no.

That was the Enemy putting that image in your mind. He is the one that has been telling you all these years that you can't really live until you lose the weight. He's also the one that has told you it's only the food or the diet that will get you through the rough times in life. Wrong.

Our God is why this guide is about God and not your weight or the food. The Enemy has been working hard enough outside of these pages to distract you so we aren't going to let him do that here. In 12-step we say, "The disease is out there doing push-ups." It's here that we are going to focus on healing you heart. It's here where you can let God do the work He does best. Get ready, because I'm sure the Enemy knows you are reading this.

He will probably launch some attacks at you. But we're going to prepare you, and I'm just going to recommend right now that you study Ephesians 6, especially verses 10–18, where it talks about the armor of God because you are going to need all of it.

In the meantime, I want you to look at Matthew 16. Jesus was sharing with Peter how He was going to die, and Peter was just saying he didn't think He would ever die, which Jesus knew wasn't true because it's the main reason He was sent. In verse 23, *"Jesus turne٠ an٠ sai٠ to Peter, 'Get behin٠ me, Satan! You are a stumbling block to me; you ٠o not have in min٠ the concerns of Go٠, but merely human concerns.'"* It wasn't that Jesus thought Peter was actually Satan. It was that Jesus could see the Enemy was trying to use Him as a weapon to divert the greater plan, and Jesus called him out.

Now, that doesn't mean you are going to walk around saying "Get behind me, Satan!" all the time. But sometimes when you are really getting attacked, you may just have to say it, "Get behind me, Satan!"

I know it may sound crazy to you, but the Enemy has had you distracted for far too long. It's time to set your mind on God.

If you feel like this is overwhelming and it feels like you may be in an even deeper pit with this than you thought, just be patient with God's process. Trust that He will pull you out if that's what you want. If He did that very thing for me fourteen years ago on the floor of my apartment, He will absolutely do it for you too.

I waited patiently for the LORD;
he turned to me and heard my cry.
He lifted me out of the slimy pit,
out of the mud and mire;
he set my feet upon a rock
and gave me a firm place to stand. (Psalm 40:1–2)

A Little Bit About the 12 Steps

An important disclaimer: if you are fortunate enough to work through this book in a community or with a friend, you will need some spiritual boundaries. This is not a place to share or promote weight loss programs or how much weight you've lost. Although that's inspiring for some people, it can be triggering for others. It's also not a place to discuss food except in general terms. You are welcome to discuss those privately with your sponsor, but the community aspect is for sharing what you are learning or struggling with as you process your thoughts and emotions on the journey with God regardless of those things.

Now, remember in the beginning the three things I wanted you to get: the Bible, *The Big Book of Alcoholics Anonymous*, and the journal? I want to talk to you a little bit about that *Big Book* (as we call it for short). We are going to be doing much more with the Bible because that is *the* ultimate truth. *"For everything that was written in the past was written to teach us, so that through the endurance taught in the Scriptures and the encouragement they provide we might have hope"* (Romans 15:4). There are people in 12-step recovery who see the *Big Book* as their book for life that will never even approach the Bible and that's their choice. But those of us who want to seek the Lord will pick up the Bible, knowing there is no replacement for that Word of God. The *Big Book* has simply been a way to get us back to Him and keep us out of the pit of our addictions.

One thing I want to note: you may or may not identify with the idea of food being an addiction. Either way it's fine. Only you can know if you do, and you can attend a meeting if that feels right to you. For the purpose of this book, we're simply using the *Big Book* as a reference tool. It is not a replacement for working a program or going to 12-step meetings. Some of you reading this may already be in the fellowship of 12-step. Some of you may not. Wherever you are, I hope it becomes a resource for you to identify what may be disordered eating or an addiction to food or dieting so you can break out of it with God's help.

If you don't know, the original 12-step program is Alcoholics Anonymous. It was founded by two men who struggled with the disease themselves, Dr. Bob S. and Bill W. They got together and found a power greater than themselves, which became what is called "Higher Power" in the program. They recovered together. God was working in the early days of that program and continues to work miracles through it today.

The reason it works for so many is because it's a spiritual program that is not attached to any religion of any kind. I can tell you I am sure grateful for that, because if it were, I probably wouldn't have walked through the doors. I felt so distant from God when I started that it took me quite a while to renew that trust, build that connection, and build an eventual relationship with God. What I have today is something I never would have dreamed of, and I truly don't believe I'd be the strong believer I am today if I didn't have that neutral space to grow up in Him.

I mentioned that in Alcoholics Anonymous there are 12 steps. I'm not going to go into all of them because that's something you can study with a sponsor in the program or with a mentor if you keep it in your church. But there are a few you should know about. The first one is: "We admitted we were powerless over alcohol—that our lives had become unmanageable."[2] (For the purposes of our discussion, you can insert *food* where it says *alcohol*.)

The word *powerlessness* can be triggering to some people because they think of it as a sign of weakness. That's the way the world has defined it. But God works differently. He shows up in our weakness. In recovery, admitting powerlessness means you are admitting what you don't have power over so you can focus on what you actually *can* change. You've probably heard of it, but in recovery the Serenity Prayer by Reinhold Niebuhr is often used, "God, grant me the serenity to accept the things I cannot change, the courage to change the things I can, and the wisdom to know the difference."

There is power in that prayer.

The greatness of a man's power is the measure of his surren♦er.
—William Booth

You've been surrendering for a long time to the Enemy's lies about how food and weight are the answer. Now you are going to surrender your belief in them to the God who can do much more with your surrender.

Step 2 says, "Came to believe that a power greater than ourselves could restore us to sanity."[3] You and I both know how crazy-making that food and weight obsession can be. That's why you are here looking for God's help. All this is saying is that you are starting to believe God (not those things) can take away that obsession.

Then in Step 3, we "made a decision to turn our will and our lives over to the care of God as we understood Him."[4] This one reminds me of James 4:7, *"Submit yourselves, then, to Go♦. Resist the ♦evil, an♦ he will flee from you."*

This is really the action step where you are basically saying, "OK, I know I'm powerless, God. I'm ready for your help." It's where your talk becomes the walk. We submit to that power greater than ourselves instead of that obsession or addiction. If you wonder why it says, "God as we understood him," that's what I was referring to earlier. It's a space for people of any background to come and not be pressured to believe a certain way so they can grow in their faith. Just like each person has their own relationship with God, this step gives people the space to find what that might look like for them.

One more note, what I say here is how I interpret the *Big Book* and how it's worked for me. There are millions of other people who've done this program that may see it differently. All I'm sharing is my perspective and my testimony.

I know all of this may seem heavy and deep. But to change the game, you've got to think differently. You've got to go deeper than the surface to get to the root. There is a saying in the program that is helpful to remember because it's really all we need: "One day at a time (ODAT)." Just like Luke 11:3 says, *"Give us each day our daily bread."*

If you doubt God can handle your baggage, read Matthew 11:28–30: *"Come to me, all you who are weary and burdened, and I will give you rest. Take my yoke upon you and learn from me, for I am gentle and humble in heart, and you will find rest for your souls. For my yoke is easy and my burden is light."*

James 4:8 says, *"Come near to God and he will come near to you. Wash your hands, you sinners, and purify your hearts, you double-minded."* He knows we're not perfect. *"For all have sinned and fall short of the glory of God"* (Romans 3:23). He's not afraid of the weight of our baggage. You know what He says?

> For I am the LORD your God
>> who takes hold of your right hand
> and says to you, Do not fear;
>> I will help you. (Isaiah 41:13)

So grab ahold of His hand and let Him guide you.

Father God, I pray that you give the person reading this the courage to see how much you want to help them change for good. Give them eyes to see their destructive patterns so they can break them with your strength and power. I pray that you would replace their desire for food or weight loss with a greater desire to know you. I pray they see the power in surrender so that you can do what you do best. Lord, show them the steps laid out for them as they walk. Give them the courage to take those steps boldly. In Jesus's name I pray. Amen.

Part I

Changing Your Mindset

Do not conform to the pattern of this world, but be transformed by the renewing of your mind. Then you will be able to test and approve what God's will is—his good, pleasing and perfect will.

—Romans 12:2

Chapter 1

When God Meets You Where You Are

So ⸱o not fear, for I am with you;
⸱o not be ⸱ismaye⸱, for I am your Go⸱.
I will strengthen you an⸱ help you;
I will uphol⸱ you with my righteous right han⸱.
—Isaiah 41:10

A few years ago, I was hiking in Sedona, Arizona, with a group of fellow life coaches. We were in Boynton Canyon behind the Enchantment Resort. I was about two-years sober at the time and dealing with discord in one of my primary relationships. I was intentionally trying to listen for God's voice.

At one point I looked down to see this rock on the trail. I leaned down to pick it up and was amazed at how much it felt like I was holding someone else's hand. Then I realized it was what God was using to remind me that He would always be there. To this day, I pick up rocks when we go up north to Leland, Michigan, from our home in Niles, Michigan. I collect heart-shaped ones, too, that remind me of His love. God gives us little reminders every day. No matter what season we're in, He's there reaching out His right hand. Do you notice it?

Even if you've felt abandoned or alone, Deuteronomy 31:6 reminds us to *"Be strong an⸱ courageous. Do not be afrai⸱ or terrifie⸱ because of them, for the* LORD *your Go⸱ goes with you; he will never leave you nor forsake you."*

When you look at these Scriptures, it's amazing to think how much we actually run away from God when we need Him most.

Whether we're using food, exercise, or diets, He waits for us to be ready to say, "I need you, God." For reflection now or later, do you know all the ways you've run away from God?

I know that for me overexercising was a big one when I was a marathoner. The constant running (literally and figuratively) kept me distracted from what was going on inside. In my last job at the White House during President George W. Bush's time in office, I was under the most stress yet. I started having panic attacks every day before staff meetings.

That's when I started to notice the Lord meeting me where I was because I had this feeling that it wasn't healthy for me to be there anymore. Do you recognize times in your life when God led you away from old habits or out of places that weren't healthy for you?

When I was three-years sober, my father passed away in an instant. In the days and weeks after that, I could barely eat and thought, "What a miracle. I don't care about food anymore." That's when the Enemy slowly but surely started to creep back in via food. I'd have a dessert here or there and think, "Oh, I'm good."

I was using my food plan (tell you more about that soon), not binge eating or overexercising, just adding. I was giving myself permission (remember that for later) to eat extra, often in the form of carbs and sugar. Many in the program would call it a relapse. Maybe it was. Whatever it was, all I know is that God once again met me right where I was.

Fast-forward nine years. I got married, became a stepmom, helped raise three stepchildren, and tried for three years to have a baby. It was a challenging season to say the least. In that time, my weight went up. Eventually, we were blessed to get pregnant. Then I spent the entire pregnancy getting sick. Many of the things I loved on my food plan made me sick. I really had to trust God and not believe the Enemy's lies. I had to believe that God would help me find the right foods to eat, that my daughter would be OK, and remind myself that this was only for a season. I believe this went like it did because of the work I'd done to get closer to God in recovery. When Ellie was born, that season of sickness ended, but I continued to eat some unhealthy stuff using the excuse that I was nursing. I was even beginning to accept that my body was the size it was supposed to be. But God had a different plan.

On April 28, 2020, about a month into the beginning of the pandemic, I was led to some life-changing Scripture. At a time when everyone was starting to turn to food in isolation, God took me in the opposite direction. I wasn't sitting there going, "Hey, I want to take this opportunity to lose weight." I literally was not even thinking about it.

I wondered if He knew I didn't want to pass down an unhealthy relationship with food to my daughter. All I know is that I wanted to be the best mom I could be to this beautiful miracle of a girl, Elianah, whose name means "God answered our prayer."

It happened on a Saturday night while my husband was laying Ellie down. I opened the Bible to read the following verses. I'd read them before, but this time it was like they were coming off the page—a Word *on* time.

These were the first two verses.

"I have the right to ·o anything," you say—but not everything is beneficial. "I have the right to ·o anything"—but not everything is constructive. (1 Corinthians 10:23)

"I have the right to ·o anything," you say—but not everything is beneficial. "I have the right to ·o anything"—but I will not be mastere· by anything. (1 Corinthians 6:12)

The next three:

*It is for free·om that Christ has set us free. Stan· firm, then, an·
·o not let yourselves be bur·ene· again by a yoke of slavery.*
(Galatians 5:1)

*You who are trying to be justifie· by the law have been alienate·
from Christ; you have fallen away from grace.* (Galatians 5:4)

*You, my brothers an· sisters, were calle· to be free. But ·o not
use your free·om to in·ulge the flesh; rather, serve one another
humbly in love.* (Galatians 5:13)

There was that word *permission* again. I liked being able to eat
whatever I wanted whenever I felt like it. I liked giving myself permission. But the Lord was revealing to me that it wasn't good, constructive, or beneficial for me anymore. Immediately my heart started
to change. I wanted to be more obedient to Him than to satisfy my
flesh. Then I thought about the chocolate-covered peanut butter bars
that kept me feeling OK during my pregnancy. They didn't need to be
consumed now just because I was breastfeeding and hungry.

Then I thought about the next three verses and asked myself,
"Why are you using your freedom in Christ to give yourself permission to eat what you feel like when God wants so much more
for you than that?"

It's like God was presenting me with this fork (ironically) in
the road: "You can go this way or that way, but you have to make a
choice." Give yourself permission to keep eating or operate in your
freedom in Christ and give Him permission to work through you.

In that moment, the choice was easy. I love the Lord and
wanted to serve Him, not myself. God had met me where I was
again, and I didn't even know I was ready for it.

You will see His purposes for us are so much greater than our physical desires. Doing His will is greater than what we feel like doing. What we feel like doing is minuscule and often short-term compared to the everlasting power of having God in our lives.

That night made me realize God had a greater plan for me. I knew right away this journey was going to serve as a road map for mothers just like you. There is no way I'd be writing this guide if He hadn't done what He did in my heart. Glory to God.

If I hadn't been in the Word of God over time, I wouldn't have seen that the Lord was offering me a way out. I just hadn't seen it until then. Now, am I saying this is exactly how God will do it for you? No. What I am saying is that if you come to know the Lord and His Word and you pray to overcome this lifelong struggle, He will reveal himself to you and give you a way out. First Corinthians 10:13 says it best, *"No temptation has overtaken you except what is common to mankin*. *An* *Go* *is faithful; he will not let you be tempte* *beyon* *what you can bear. But when you are tempte*, *he will also provi*e *a way out so that you can en*ure it."*

He is your way out. Will it be difficult? Yes, absolutely, it will be. But the game changer is this time you are going to do it with Him, not just with your faulty willpower.

Here's another promise from Scripture to remind you that when it gets tough, He isn't going anywhere.

But now, this is what the LORD says—
    he who create *you, Jacob,*
    he who forme *you, Israel:*
*"Do not fear, for I have re*eeme* *you;*
    I have summone *you by name; you are mine.*
When you pass through the waters,
    I will be with you;
an *when you pass through the rivers,*

they will not sweep over you.
When you walk through the fire,
  you will not be burned;
  the flames will not set you ablaze." (Isaiah 43:1–2)

Or how about this one from *The Message*? *"GOD met me more than halfway, he freed me from my anxious fears"* (Psalm 34:4).

Father God, I pray whoever is reading this senses that you are meeting them right where they are in this moment. I pray you would reveal to them your strength in their weakness around food. Give them the willingness to surrender to your will over their willpower. Remind them that no matter how big this storm feels, you aren't going anywhere. Give them the insight to see where, when, and how you are meeting them where they are.

Be with them, Lord. In Jesus's name. Amen.

Chapter 2

Finding Your *Why*

Fin• your why an• you'll fin• your way.

—John C. Maxwell

You know that question you always ask yourself when you gain the weight again? It sounds something like, "Why can't I just keep this weight off?" or "What is wrong with me?" Sometimes you ask God something like, "Why won't you just let me keep the weight off?" Thankfully that's not the *why* I'm talking about here.

I'm talking about the *why* that motivates you. Why do you want to do something different? Think about past weight-loss experiences. What were your motivating factors? Maybe it was a medical issue, and your doctor said that you had to lose the weight. Maybe you wanted to get to a certain number on the scale or a certain pants size. Maybe you saw a picture of yourself, and it freaked you out. Maybe it was a reunion coming up or a wedding. Whatever the reasons have been, they were the ones that worked at the time. Those were good goals. But they were temporary ones. When God is your focus, your goals become God-driven. His eternal love becomes the force that gives you the desire to live for Him, making you no longer limited to short-term goals of events or occasions.

This time, I believe God wants health in mind and body to last for you. His plans are greater than you looking good for a reunion. He wants you to be the best vessel you can be for His glory. Jeremiah 29:11 promises, *"For I know the plans I have for you,' •eclares the* LORD, *'plans to prosper you an• not to harm you, plans to give you hope an• a future.'"* Do you realize this? Do you believe your life might be worth more than a number on the scale? *"For we are Go•'s han•iwork, create• in Christ Jesus to •o goo• works, which Go• prepare• in a•vance for us to •o"* (Ephesians 2:10). God created you *on* purpose *for* a purpose, and it's way bigger than a life focused on food or weight loss.

With God's better plans for you in mind, let's put down the obsession with food or weight and think about what stirs your soul. What excites you? What breaks your heart open and makes you want to help others? What ignites a fire in you? What are you passionate about?

Let's start with your natural abilities. Do you know you have a skill that comes naturally to you, and you do it well? For me, I believe that skill is writing. It took me years and getting into recovery to realize that. But I'm grateful I did. For a friend of mine, it's baking. She makes beautiful cookies and cakes that blow my mind. I really don't know how she does it. (Yes, one of my closest friends is a baker.) But it's obvious she has a gift. We are all gifted in something because God gave us that skill.

The other thing is there may be something you've been through or a certain season of your life that was tough, and God wants you to help others through it. You may not want to talk about it yet and that's OK. God may just want to use it to help another person. But He can't do that until you are willing to seek Him more for deeper healing and share your testimony so He gets the glory. Getting into recovery helped me see that the time period from college into my twenties was one of the hardest for me. I realized I wanted to help young women navigate that season of life so they didn't have to make the same mistakes I did. As quickly as I could, I got a life coach certification and helped as many as I could. Then God gave me three stepchildren whose upbringing became the focus of my life for a season, and God did some serious healing on me. It made me realize how much I wanted to help young women who've been through things such as their parents' divorce and other situations that can make it hard to grow up emotionally.

It's amazing what God does when you are open to being a vessel for His grace. He puts people in your life that are walking almost the same road as you that need to hear about your healing. They need to hear how you've walked through the big things. It happens so often for me that it's made my coaching more of a spiritual mentoring because I get to share how God changed my life during the roughest seasons. I hope I get to do it till the day He calls me home.

My most important *why* is my family. I want to keep walking this journey for them. When Elianah is ready to ask me questions, I want to be real about what happened and about God's healing. I want to keep walking it for my husband so we can have a marriage that glorifies God. That is a miracle in itself because for a long time this child of divorce thought she might never get married, let alone have stepchildren or be a mom. God is a miracle worker who is worth seeking.

But seek first his kingdom and his righteousness, and all these things will be given to you as well. (Matthew 6:33)

You will seek me and find me when you seek me with all your heart. (Jeremiah 29:13)

So, seek God and let Him reveal it to you in His time.

One more thing many of you already know. But for the ones that don't, when you come to believe, you are given a spiritual gift. *"Now to each one the manifestation of the Spirit is given for the common good"* (1 Corinthians 12:7). There are many books on it that you can read to inquire more, but God puts it there for a reason—so you share it with other believers. I'm pretty sure mine is exhortation (encouragement), so I try to do it as much as I can to give

God glory. I love finding out what other people's gifts are too. I recommend you find out what yours is to help you find your *why.*

God knew exactly what He was doing the minute He created you. In Jeremiah 1:5, the Lord says to Jeremiah, *"Before I formed you in the womb I knew you, before you were born I set you apart; I appointed you as a prophet to the nations."* Psalm 139:16 says,

> *Your eyes saw my unformed body;*
> > *all the days ordained for me were written in your book*
> > *before one of them came to be.*

So don't think for a minute God doesn't have a purpose for you.

Think of this journey as not simply stopping your focus on food and weight but as being more of whom God has called you to be. To be who God has called us to be, we have to be disciplined in mind and body. It reminds me of 1 Corinthians 9:27 NLT: *"I discipline my body like an athlete, training it to do what it should. Otherwise, I fear that after preaching to others I myself might be disqualified."*

Father God, I pray that you give the person reading this a desire to find their personal why. If it's been hidden for years, bring it back in a way that makes them desire food and diets less, so they desire to seek you more. Lord, reveal to them some of the ways you've designed them to shine brightly in this world for your glory. In Jesus's name. Amen.

Chapter 3

Getting Honest with Yourself

Then Jesus sai◦ to his ◦isciples: "Therefore I tell you, ◦o not worry about your life, what you will eat; or about your bo◦y, what you will wear."

—Luke 12:22

Sometimes we worry so much about what others think or what we'll eat or when we'll get our workout in, that we forget God's reminder that we do not have to worry. When we're overly worried about issues like these, we can't get real with ourselves or God. That's why we have to be honest with ourselves. I have a sticker on the back of my car that reads, "Life is a journey . . . enjoy the ride."

It's a great reminder for me and the people behind me to take life a little less seriously. I could never do that before recovery because I was too busy maintaining the surface and avoiding those feelings. But recovery has given me the tremendous gift of learning to be present in the moment and honest with myself—feelings, thoughts, and all. If I'm too focused on the future or worse, dreaming of how I'll get to live once I lose the weight, then I'm not in the present moment. In the program, we call this "rigorous honesty" with ourselves, with God, and with our sponsor or mentor.

When you aren't picking up the food or focusing on the diet to numb or run, you can do more than just feel the feelings. You become more sensitive to when you are in the wrong or when something doesn't feel right. You just get more honest. It's important to maintain that honesty. It's not always easy. But it's important because when you are digging beneath the surface, you can't operate on the surface. I know that when I'm honest, I crave the time with God to get honest with Him. I have to talk to God about the stuff that is bothering me, and that's when I go to my chair, get in the Word or a devotion, and write to God. I cherish that time, especially when I don't get to do it as often as I like.

I also appreciate the time I get to talk to my sponsor every week, as well as my dearest friend at church. Both keep me accountable to what's going on in my life. Deeper relationships are such a huge part of this journey and so worth it, especially when you are on social media. If you see someone share about their next fad diet, you'll be over here working through the real stuff, knowing you are getting stronger physically, mentally, and spiritually with each day. Just keep going. Keep being in the moment and facing those challenges with God's help, your mentor/sponsor, and your community.

Then say the Serenity Prayer to yourself as often as you must to remember what you can and can't control.

> *Go• grant me the serenity to accept the things I cannot change, the courage to change the things I can, an• the wis•om to know the •ifference.*
>
> —Reinhold Niebuhr

If that's not enough, pick up *The Big Book of Alcoholics Anonymous* and read some stories in the back. You will be amazed at the stories you relate to that can give you the courage to be honest.

Again, replace that word *alcohol* with food and it can really give you powerful insight and remind you that you aren't alone. We will talk more about that in a little bit. I just wanted to give you this brief chapter as a reminder to keep that honesty going. Your courage will increase in this process, and it will be beautiful.

Father God, you already know everything about us. You know every detail of our lives. You also know we can still have trouble being honest with ourselves, with others, and with you. Lord, I just ask you to help the person reading this to have a desire and willingness to be more honest in those areas. Remind them that you are trustworthy and give them that person who can be their sounding board when it's time to be rigorously honest. Thank you, Lord, for giving us the ability to be honest with you. In Jesus's name. Amen.

Part II

Turning Over the Food and Weight to God

Then Jesus ⬩eclare⬩, "I am the brea⬩ of life. Whoever comes to me will never go hungry, an⬩ whoever believes in me will never be thirsty."

—John 6:35

Chapter 4

Abstinence and Finding a Food Plan

To many, total abstinence is easier than perfect moderation.

—St. Augustine

When we talk about abstinence here, we are referring to ceasing to eat those foods on your trigger-food list that keep you from seeking God. I realize that there are programs that are all about moderation. If you are someone that can do that, then that's great for you. But many of us cannot, so when we're ready, we have to make the choice to stop trying to use moderation and just let go of those trigger foods.

You may have heard the term abstinence before related to sex or alcohol or some other behavior. But here we are talking about food. (I'll tell you more about the food plan in a minute). Here is how the 12-step program Overeaters Anonymous defines the meaning of abstinence on its website: "Abstinence is the action of refraining from compulsive eating and compulsive food behaviors while working towards or maintaining a healthy body weight. Spiritual, emotional, and physical recovery is the result of living and working the Overeaters Anonymous 12 Step program on a daily basis."[5]

You may consider it fasting, especially if that's what you know from Scripture as a way to connect more deeply to the Lord. "Fasting is a grace that significantly increases our receptivity to the Lord's voice and His Word."[6]

Fasting can be a tricky word because it can be associated with eating disorders like anorexia or orthorexia because of the restricting aspect. If that's something you struggle with, I recommend you see a professional (will talk more about that later). But right now, this is about the spiritual aspect that keeps you out of the foods, not just to lose the weight like the diet industry likes to use them but to just put them down. Abstaining is an act of offering to God those things we put above Him. Metaphorically speaking, we are taking our hands off what we can't control so that God can be in control.

This section is where the rubber meets the road. This is where you have to get serious about not making this about a diet. It is not about cutting out food groups that your body needs like proteins, vegetables, grains, and healthy fats. If you have allergies, that's something between you and your doctor. It is about stopping the behavior patterns related to your compulsive eating that keep you from a healthy life.

I'm amazed when I see a commercial for a diet where you don't have to give up your favorite foods, like it's a reward. I look at that and say to myself, "No, thanks," because I know that is not what I want to be doing. I don't want to be picking up that very thing that kept me distracted in the first place. Also, there isn't enough of it to fill the hole inside that only God can fill.

The truth is if you have an inkling that your struggle with food may be an addiction, you are going to have to face the beast every day. You've got to have a battle plan with the foods that are your weakness. Here's the other thing: you can't just say to yourself, "I'm going to give this up." You and I both know where that gets you. Choosing to abstain or fast is your demonstration of faith to God that you trust Him over yourself.

James 2:17–18 says, *"Thus also faith by itself, if it •oes not have works, is •ea•. But someone will say, You have faith, an• I have works.' Show me your faith without your works, an• I will show you my faith by my works"* (NKJV).

Whether you are in a Bible study, a biblically based support group, or you choose to get into Overeaters Anonymous (OA), you will learn more about this surrender. (There are a number of meetings listed in the back of the book.) You will be shocked how many people have gone through very similar struggles with food, and you will feel less alone.

Know this: everyone's abstinence looks different. So be patient with yourself as you figure it out.

One thing I will tell you is that you will need to work with someone to figure out what that looks like for you. The first person will probably be your sponsor if you choose to do 12-step or someone you can trust if you are in a group at church. Then you have to get serious.

If you have some food program that works for you and keeps your weight in check, that's great. If it keeps you grounded, I'm not going to stop you. But if you are still using all those trigger foods, they are going to be hard to put down as well as the diet you may be on with them.

What are those trigger foods? More than likely they are any combination of sugar, flour, or salt. Give yourself time with this. It helps sometimes to start looking at the labels in your pantry and in your fridge. Pick up some of the foods you frequently eat. Read the label. Is there some form of sugar or flour in the first four ingredients? Then you've got something for your list. You will probably be shocked at some of the foods that end up on it.

Real recovery is complete lifestyle change.
—Unknown

Whether you are including 12-step recovery in this or not, you are recovering from the lifestyle of constantly dieting and attempting to control your food yourself. In order to make that lifestyle change you will have to do more than talk to a sponsor or mentor. You will have to get what we call in the program, a "food plan." Now I know not everyone will do this. But if you are obsessive about controlling your food or you are all over the place, this could be your lifesaver. Let me just tell you a little more about it.

The best way I can summarize it is: the food plan gives you boundaries around food so you can recover. It is one of the absolute greatest gifts of recovery and its best-kept secret. It is your daily commitment to God and the program that you are committed to. Essentially, it's like a prescription for your recovery. By using a food plan, you can function better, much like a person who suffers from anxiety who takes medication.

This is your medicine. The beautiful thing about it is that it's all natural. It is what will keep you physically grounded so you can focus on being rigorously honest about what's in your heart.

I know this is not easy stuff. I am well aware. You will definitely be craving those trigger foods as you start this, which is why you need support and a mentor/sponsor to be there. (This next one is for all my perfectionists). You are not going to do this perfectly, especially at the beginning. You'll be like a baby learning how to walk. You'll get up and fall down a ton. Just remember. This is not about behavior modification. This is spiritual transformation. You are going much deeper now, into the roots of your soul. Again, be patient with yourself. Know that God isn't beating you up. He is cheering you on. He wants this for you because He wants you to be more devoted to Him than those foods that don't work for you anymore. Recovery is not about reaching a goal weight. It is a lifestyle. Changing your lifestyle takes time.

What I can tell you is that once you get it, the longer you stay abstinent, the clearer your mind gets, the better your body feels, and the closer you feel to God. God willing, the weight will come off of you *not* because it's your goal but because it's a by-product of getting on a food plan and working on the heart stuff. Over the course of almost two years, I've lost fifty pounds in a slow, healthy way.

The other thing about getting on a food plan is that you are going to do something crazy. It's called—feel. You are going to be feeling your emotions, not stuffing them down. This is another reason you need the support community and the sponsor/mentor because you will need a navigator. You will likely feel some sadness that will be like grief because it's like you've lost your best friend. You may even feel frustrated because you'll just want to do what you usually do but you can't. You will feel vulnerable, almost like you don't have skin. But I promise, you will get stronger. Remember Eleanor Roosevelt's words: "You gain strength, courage, and confidence by every experience in which you really stop to look fear in the face."[7] And know that God will be there. *"God is our refuge and strength, an ever-present help in trouble"* (Psalm 46:1).

I know this is scary. But believe me, I would not be sharing this if it didn't work. It may take you a few times. But when it clicks, the food plan feels like freedom. It is absolutely awesome to not have to think about food all day. What's even better is that you don't have to engage in conversations about dieting or scroll your news feed, seeing before and after pictures, wishing you had what someone else has. It's almost like God protects you from it in the process. It is freeing to actually be able to eat foods you enjoy that keep you fueled AND full.

I have gotten to know my body so well that I can tell when I haven't had enough protein, fat, veggies, or carbs. It's like my body turns its check-engine light on. "Whoa, we didn't get enough of those nutrients." You know what else is freeing? To be able to walk by those foods in the pantry, the grocery store, or in a restaurant and have no desire to eat them.

Another important element is measuring your food. I think more people do this today. But for me, it helps a ton with my portion sizes because I'm one of those people who tends to want more. The food scale keeps you honest. You may be someone who tends to restrict. The scale helps you follow your food plan and get what you need so you don't get back into that disordered eating.

Measuring cups and tablespoons are another thing. I use a tablespoon for things like salad dressing and a measuring cup for things like oatmeal. It just keeps me confident that I'm getting what I need. Otherwise I'd be overthinking it.

You know what else? You may find a newfound love for cooking in a healthy way. This one shocks me still today. My family actually likes my cooking.

God is so good. He took this little girl who lived for food, healed her toxic relationship with it, and made it one of her love languages. I don't know what your relationship with food has been like, but I want you to believe that God can turn it around and use it for good.

Another thing about the food plan and beyond. If you want to know how to get on a food plan, here's what I suggest: if you are doing 12-step, ask someone in your meetings who they'd recommend. Some people just have their sponsor do it. But I believe that having one prescribed to you by a nutritionist is a little better. They can work with you based on where you are personally and where you want to be to get you what you need. Plus, they are the professionals and sometimes that's what you need—someone who is the actual expert.

I know with the number of diets we've all been on, we feel like experts. But we are not professionals. If you are not doing OA or another 12-step program, you can search online. I recommend finding someone who is well versed in disordered eating. Maybe they work with people recovering from eating disorders or food addictions. Don't get too attached to that concept or label. It's just someone who has a better grasp on the emotional side of eating, which is a good thing. You may be someone who already has a great plan you want to use that helps you remove those foods. That's great. Do what works for you. Just watch for that old diet or restrictive thinking. If you are wondering about the cost, I can tell you a session with this person will cost you way less than all the diets you've been on or food you've purchased to overeat.

Lastly, there is a chance you may be reading this and finding it extremely challenging. If so, you may have more going on internally than you realize. Treatment, either inpatient or outpatient, may be something you need to consider. It's OK if that's the case. Sometimes we need to get away from it all to get comprehensive care. There are some wonderful places you can go. Seek God's guidance and support from people who understand so you don't feel alone walking through the process. One thing I would recommend is finding a place that helps you learn how to make it a lifestyle. You don't want to walk out of treatment and have nowhere to go. If you can find somewhere that folds going to 12-step meetings into it, that would be great. Maybe it's more Scripture-based. Whatever it is, the exit strategy is just as important as the entry.

However you approach this, I just pray that you

> *Trust in the LORD with all your heart*
> > *an• lean not on your own un•erstan•ing;*
> *in all your ways submit to him,*
> > *an• he will make your paths straight.*
> *Do not be wise in your own eyes;*
> > *fear the LORD an• shun evil.*
> *This will bring health to your bo•y*
> > *an• nourishment to your bones.* (Proverbs 3:5–8)

Father Go•, I pray that whoever is rea•ing this can fin• the courage to change what they can about their relationship to foo•. Help them to embrace the concept of abstinence so they can turn the foo• over to you. Help them fin• a foo• plan to help give them lasting abstinence an• walk through the emotional an• mental aspects of the program. Thank you, Lor•, for your gifts. In Jesus's name. Amen.

Chapter 5

Getting Real About Your Food

If you know the enemy an◆ know yourself, you nee◆ not fear the result of a hun◆re◆ battles.

—Sun Tzu, Chinese military strategist and
author of *The Art of War*

I wish I could say we're done talking about food after discussing abstinence and the food plan. But we're not. This is where I believe a lot of diets stop—at behavior modification. They give you what you need to do, tell you what not to do, but don't really help you with why you were going to those unhealthy foods in the first place. Oftentimes, they just tell you different ways of getting your "fix" in lower calories ways. Doesn't work. Remember, we are doing it differently here. We're going deeper.

What you will do next is name the foods you can't stop eating. You started it when you began to notice those trigger foods. Now, we're going to get to the substance of why they are a weakness for you because the better you know your weaknesses, the stronger you are.

There is a concept I've found in recovery that can really help. If you imagine that you have an allergic reaction to those foods you can't stop eating, you can understand your habits a little better. It really helps me set a boundary because I know how my body responds, and how hard it is to get it back. *The Big Book of Alcoholics Anonymous* says this about it in the Introduction section called, "The Doctor's Opinion," on page xxx[8] (remember to think of it in terms of food). "All these, and many others, have one symptom in common: they cannot start drinking without developing the phenomenon of craving. This phenomenon, as we have suggested, may be the manifestation of an allergy which differentiates these people, and sets them apart as a distinct entity. It has never been, by any treatment with which we are familiar, permanently eradicated. The only relief we have to suggest is entire abstinence."

That craving is like an allergy of both the mind and body. When we taste the trigger food, it sets off a chain reaction in our mind and body to crave more. If we keep these foods in our diet, we keep the cravings going. If we try to just restrict them with a diet, we return to them with a vengeance because we haven't realized the allergic reaction they set into motion. This is why we practice entire abstinence. We must abstain from those foods that set off the reaction in our bodies.

I mentioned earlier what those foods typically look like. Sugar and flour are the most common. Salt can be a problem too. Whatever these foods are for you, get honest by starting to write them down. Practice studying those labels with sugar and flour in the first four ingredients and toss them or don't buy them. Your sponsor or nutritionist can help you with this.

I know for me, if I allow sugar or flour in my diet, which are my two trigger foods, my cravings are pretty constant. I always want more of those in some form simply because it's in my system. I can't walk down an aisle at the grocery store where my trigger food is without buying it. I can't get it out of my mind or tame the physical craving for it. I need it. I think I can't survive unless I have it. That's how I know it's gotten bad because there is no way one day of not eating it will change anything. I just know that overpowering physical and mental craving will get me unless I have given it to God. When God's got it, I can walk by those things in the store or in my kitchen and know "It's not worth it."

It doesn't mean I don't think "Oh, it would be nice to have that," but the consequences far outweigh the craving the longer I stay abstinent. I don't care how good it looks or how much I can almost taste it in my mouth. It's just not worth it. That's how I tame the cravings in recovery. My mind is stronger, and my body feels better when I'm not, as I like to think, "regularly feeding the beast." The longer I don't pick them up, the more I rely on God and trust Him to help me navigate those cravings instead of depending on my own willpower.

I know some of you who will not be able to completely clear these out of your house. I get it. I have a husband who enjoys sweets and a toddler too. It's hard to avoid. One thing that has helped me is to simply keep being honest with myself and understand that it's me that has to deal with this, not them. It's not like when I'm on a diet, feeling deprived because I can't enjoy the sugary foods with them. In fact, not partaking in eating those sugary foods is what allows me to be free to enjoy their company instead of worrying about what I'm missing.

It shouldn't come as a surprise to you that sugar can be addictive. Dr. Mark Hyman, a physician and the *New York Times* best-selling author of multiple books such as *The Bloo꞊ Sugar Solution: The UltraHealthy Program for Losing Weight, Preventing Disease, an꞊ Feeling Great Now!* says, "Sugar is the core ingredient used by the food industry to make bad ingredients (processed flour and chemicals) taste good."[9] There are multiple books on the addictive power of sugar.

Now, you wonder why I mentioned flour. According to Harvard School of Public Health, carbohydrates have a major effect on your blood sugar. "When people eat a food containing carbohydrates, the digestive system breaks down the digestible ones into sugar, which enters the blood. As blood sugar levels rise, the pancreas produces insulin, a hormone that prompts cells to absorb blood sugar for energy and storage."[10]

It actually processes as sugar in your body. Not everyone has an issue with it, but for those of us who do, you need to be aware. I can tell you my experience has been that consuming flour gives me the same physical and mental reaction as when I eat sugar. I can actually feel the spike in my blood sugar, and I crave more. The longer I continue to consume it, the more my blood sugar rides a roller coaster. What that does is increase my anxiety and lead to regular panic attacks. I don't know if you've ever had one, but they are not fun. The other thing is I don't just crave more of it, I am starving all the time from the drop in blood sugar. It's like my body is constantly sending a stress signal that it wants what I need, not what I want, but I can't pay attention because I'm so stuck in that craving cycle.

I know the idea of looking at how many foods you eat that are in this category can be overwhelming. Please, try not to beat yourself up or sabotage yourself. You are learning right now. Just keep the list going and make it fun. Treat it like a game, where you try to find all the foods the Enemy likes to use against you. It's almost like a game of Whac-A-Mole. Keep a list on your phone. Talk to your sponsor/mentor about them so you are accountable. Also, give yourself some credit for your bravery here. You are a warrior for doing this because you are getting into the nitty-gritty ways the Enemy likes to keep you numb.

My hope in taking you through this exercise is that you will know better the specific tactics of the Enemy in your life. No more mindless eating. He loves that. Don't give him the power. This truly is a spiritual battle in which Satan has deceived you with the foods you love to keep you physically, mentally, and spiritually sick. In case you don't believe me yet, let me just tell you a little more.

Sun Tzu said, "All warfare is based on deception."[11] Scripture says, *"And no wonder, for Satan himself masquerades as an angel of light"* (2 Corinthians 11:14). Just think about how good these foods have looked and tasted when you wanted comfort. Then think about how temporary the satisfaction is when you've finished eating. Or think about how hard it's always been to get the weight off after consuming them for a while. But what do we do? Go straight to the diet because that's just what we know.

Let me tell you a quick story. Before I went to treatment, I participated in a graduate study at the University of Notre Dame based on the book *Intuitive Eating: A Revolutionary Program that Works* by Evelyn Tribole. Over the course of about six weekly sessions, we went through, tested, and applied the concepts together with a group of us who struggled with binge eating. This program works for many people to get off the diet cycle. But it did not for me. I just didn't find that out until later, after I'd agreed to be featured in an article with pictures for the local newspaper.

A number of my headshots were featured on the cover of the section where the course was featured. When I opened it up, there was a full-page, top-to-bottom photo of me running. I was mortified. The Enemy's voice was so incredibly loud that day that it was part of the impetus for me to go to treatment. All I heard was "You are still fat." Evil. Taking a message I'd echoed in my mind since childhood, there I was at thirty years old hearing it louder than ever. I was done giving it so much power.

You've got to understand that the devil is relentless in his pursuit. His goal is to keep you defeated. "He [the devil] was a murderer from the beginning, not holding to the truth, for there is no truth in him. When he lies, he speaks his native language, for he is a liar and the father of lies" (John 8:44). As the Enemy tempts you with short-lived satisfaction of the flesh, Jesus calls him out for his lies and promises life. *"The thief comes only to steal and kill and destroy; I have come that they may have life, and have it to the full"* (John 10:10). God is for you. He wants to give you a full life. The Enemy wants to keep you small. He wants you to stay attached to those trigger foods, so you never get real victory. Don't let him have that power over your life. Give it back to God.

Father Go•, I pray you will give the person rea•ing this the knowle•ge of how the Enemy has been using trigger foo•s as a weapon. Give them the courage to hol• onto you as they •iscover these. Remin• them you are strength in their weakness, an• you will continue to be with them through this process. May they earnestly seek you. In Jesus's name. Amen.

Chapter 6

Why the Support Aspect Is So Important

Two people are better off than one, for they can help each other succee . If one person falls, the other can reach out an help. But someone who falls alone is in real trouble.

—Ecclesiastes 4:9–10 NLT

I'm a firm believer that we are meant to do this life with other people. Our bad habits love isolation because then we never get connected. Spiritual transformation works better in community because we grow when we have people alongside us who understand us and want us to get better and stay better. We need the "experience, strength and hope" (like we talk about in 12-step) of others or else we get stuck in that thinking that no one understands. People do. We just have to be willing to reach out. We need to know that other people have fought the same battles we have fought, and they have similar demons. It's one thing to have people love and support you. But it's a whole other thing to have people who understand you walking with you.

I've found that God puts those people in my life right when I need them because He wants to provide comfort to His children. It makes 2 Corinthians 1:3–4 come alive. *"Praise be to the Go and Father of our Lor Jesus Christ, the Father of compassion an the Go of all comfort, who comforts us in all our troubles, so that we can comfort those in any trouble with the comfort we ourselves receive from Go ."* Doing this work in community allows us to be a vessel for God to work and gives us the chance to find comfort in others who do the same.

A support community helps so much with getting you out of the isolation to process the emotions that come up. You don't have to wait until it's really bad. You don't have to compare yourself to others and say, "I'm not that bad," because the truth is that God wants to meet you right where you are with other people who understand. I am aware that some of you may have an idea of what you think recovery is like based on what your experience was with someone you love. Sadly, it doesn't work for everyone.

You may be someone who was deeply hurt, and that is completely understandable. But I want to challenge you to approach it with new eyes. If they didn't get better, that doesn't mean it doesn't work. There is a massive difference between someone who is active in addiction and someone who is choosing the path of recovery, and there are many who live victorious lives by choosing it. If you read the chapter "There Is a Solution" in *The Big Book of Alcoholics Anonymous*, there is a wonderful description on the first page about how we are all like "passengers of a great liner the moment after rescue from shipwreck."[12] We all share a common struggle and are choosing to overcome it together. Community is powerful, especially when you share a weakness.

There is so much hope in the common ground of those who want to get better and make the lifestyle choices to do that. Please know that I'm not promoting the program for the case of the program. I actually can't do that because we have a rule about attraction, not promotion. I am just sharing my experience, strength, and hope through this guide because that's how I can communicate best to someone who might need the help.

Next to the food plan for eating recovery, the meetings are like medicine to those of us in any kind of 12-step recovery. They keep us humble and remind us we aren't alone. They keep us strong as we navigate life. No matter what I go through, I have found that turning to my friends in recovery is just what I need to navigate the hard times. The same goes for my Christian friends. I need both to keep walking toward the Lord.

On the day my dad died, August 23, 2011, I walked into a meeting and knew there would be people who had gone through similar things who would understand how much I didn't want to escape. They kept me steady during that time. They've been there to watch me grow, and it's been pretty amazing to watch them do the same. Even though no one ever plans to be part of it, the ones who stay know the absolute blessing it is to never have to escape from life again with a substance.

Please know, this support community can absolutely happen somewhere other than 12-step. It may organically happen in your church or your community. I just wanted to share my experience of continual community through 12-step programs.

Whether you go to a meeting or keep it in your community, what you will want to do is look for a sponsor or mentor who has the type of recovery you want. They will guide you through what some consider the meaty parts of the steps. This includes steps four through nine. You can look at your *Big Book* to review those. It's where you will take what we call a personal inventory of your life—your relationships, your fears, and more in order to, as we say, "clean up your side of the street."

I realize this may sound intimidating. That's why you don't do it in a day, and it's more of a lifestyle because you work on God's healing time, not yours. I remember when I first started, I wanted to get through all of them, be done, and move to the next thing. Thankfully, I had people who showed me that's not how it works. By accepting that, I was able to start working through things and resist the urge to fight it. But you have to be ready, and your sponsor or mentor will help you with that. The beauty is they won't judge you for anything you share because they've either lived it or heard it from someone else. That, to me, was comforting.

If you do want to go to a 12-step meeting, you can consult the list in the back of this book or do an online search in your local area. There are many in person and online. There are also

Bible-based ones like Celebrate Recovery that you can use as a basis to keep the community going. You could start a meeting. There are also Life Recovery groups that have a wonderful New Living Translation version of the Bible called *The Life Recovery Bible*, which I often use.

Just be patient with your process. Know that the only requirement for membership is a desire to stop overeating. It might help to pray for God to reveal to you the meeting(s) that would work best. That helped me when I found the program I'm in today. It didn't happen right away. Believe me. I've tried many over the years in person and online. Finally, I found the one that works for me, or maybe I was just finally willing and it presented itself. I can't tell you which one works specifically for me because of the anonymity of that group, but I will tell you it's the best program I have found. I am hoping there are more groups that pop up in churches because of this book. *The Big Book* has something called "The Twelve Traditions," which have helped keep 12-step groups consistent and orderly for years. They can be a good resource.

One of the concepts discussed there is anonymity. This is *essential* for anyone who doesn't want it known they are there. I mentioned earlier that I made the choice to share my story and break my own anonymity. That's my choice. I just want you to know that when you walk into a room, you are anonymous. No one has to know your story. We only share first names. It doesn't matter if your neighbor is in the room, they are required by the twelfth tradition to not break your anonymity outside the room.

So even if you wanted to know if someone is in the program, I would not be at liberty to share that. That's up to them. The twelfth tradition states, "Anonymity is the spiritual foundation of all our traditions, ever reminding us to place principles before personalities."[13] I hope you find solace in that.

This support factor and your willingness to enter it so you can walk alongside those doing the same thing is one of the most key elements of all of this. Don't miss out on participating in it.

Father Go•, I pray the person rea•ing this fin•s within them a •esire to fin• a support community. If it's to go to a meeting, give them the courage. If it's to fin• a group in their church, help them fin• the people who will walk besi•e them. I pray a see• has been plante•, that you will give them the courage to show up when they're rea•y an• put the right people in their path to help them through it. In Jesus's name. Amen.

Part III

Dealing with Your Heart Wounds

The truly goo♦ news is that Go♦ is not a ♦istant Go♦ . . . but a Go♦ who is move♦ by our pains an♦ participates in the fullness of the human struggle.

—Henri Nouwen

Therefore, since we have a great high priest who has ascen♦e♦ into heaven, Jesus the Son of Go♦, let us hol♦ firmly to the faith we profess. For we ♦o not have a high priest who is unable to empathize with our weaknesses, but we have one who has been tempte♦ in every way, just as we are—yet he ♦i♦ not sin. Let us then approach Go♦'s throne of grace with confi♦ence, so that we may receive mercy an♦ fin♦ grace to help us in our time of nee♦.

—Hebrews 4:14–16

Chapter 7

Dealing with Your Feelings

The only feelings that do not heal are the ones you hide.

—Henri Nouwen

Let's talk about feelings. I've heard this saying in recovery and therapy: "Feelings aren't facts." Sometimes our feelings are so intense we think that they have to be facts. But we must recognize they are not. I don't know how you've run from your feelings over the years. Maybe you've tried to stuff them down with food for years, which is common for an addict. Maybe you've been a serial dieter trying to make them go away.

Either way, they never go anywhere until you face them. The longer you fight them, the longer they lie dormant in your heart. If you are someone who was taught your whole life not to reveal your feelings, it may be a foreign concept to you. That's OK. It's also OK if you've bought a ton of magazines believing what the cover says, such as "3 Easy Steps to Stop Your Emotional Eating." The world always offers us a fix.

Whenever I watch the Disney movie *Frozen*, I think, "Man, do I relate to Elsa!" (Bear with me here. I'm the mom of a three-year-old daughter.) Here is this character, Elsa, who tries to conceal her feelings for years. She's sequestered away from her sister after their parents die in a shipwreck because revealing her feelings (especially fear) will freeze everything. When she finally comes out of isolation to be coronated as queen of Arendelle, she gets upset with her sister. Through a series of events, her fear is exposed and everything freezes. She runs away to be alone. Do you ever have that feeling, like you just want to run away from everyone and feel because you're afraid you'll lose it? All the time, right?

Sometimes I'll watch my daughter have a temper tantrum and think how hard those feelings must be for a toddler. They have no clue how to process them. I don't remember those days. But I do remember hiding in my closet as a young girl and going for a drive when I finally got my license. We always want to run from our feelings. That's the beauty of recovery. You don't have to do that. Yes, you can step away and feel. But you don't have to keep them from coming.

Today, I'm grateful that I get to feel all of my feelings. Sometimes I do have to get in my car, drive, and let the tears flow. Other times I have to go for a walk. Other times I write. I have ways to process now and most importantly—I am not afraid to feel or share them.

Sadly, we live in a world that teaches one of two things: "Conceal, don't feel" like Elsa in *Frozen* or the whole concept of "Follow your heart." But look what Jeremiah 17:9 says,

The heart is deceitful above all things
and beyond cure.
Who can understand it?

God can. Verse 10 says, *"I the LORD search the heart and examine the mind."* We don't have to conceal them, avoid them, or let them run our lives because we have a God who can help us navigate them. They are a beautiful part of how He designed us. I've been told I'm too sensitive before, but now I know it's like a superpower. It's a privilege to feel emotions, and it's a blessing to know the Lord can carry me through them. While the rest of the world is trusting their feelings alone, you get to trust in the Lord. As the waves come and go, He just says, "Trust me. I've got you."

Look at the story of Peter from Matthew 14 when the disciples saw Jesus walking on water. They were scared. In verse 27, Jesus said, *"Take courage! It is I. Don't be afraid."* Peter responded in verse 28: *"Lord, if it's you, . . . tell me to come to you on the water."* In verse 29, Jesus said, *"Come."* Then Peter got down out of the boat and walked on water toward Jesus.

In verses 30–33: *"But when [Peter] saw the wind, he was afraid and, beginning to sink, cried out, 'Lord, save me!' Immediately Jesus reached out his hand and caught him. 'You of little faith,' he said, 'why did you doubt?' And when they climbed into the boat, the wind died down. Then those who were in the boat worshiped him, saying, 'Truly you are the Son of God.'"*

So remember that when you fear. If Peter could trust God, you can too. Believe me, I've had to do the same thing many times. The only way we overcome our fears is by walking through them with God's help. There is a reason "Fear not" is in the Bible 365 times. You can be reminded of it every day. That doesn't mean you should never fear. We all do. But trust God in the midst of those fears. Believe Him when He says, "Fear not." The things you are learning here will help you with that because getting more honest about your food will help you hear Him more clearly and trust Him. You and I both know we're not trusting God's goodness when we're trusting the food or the diet. Courage doesn't come by doing these things. It comes by trusting God as you keep walking.

I am aware of how big those emotional waves can get. They still happen to me regularly. I am also aware of how long those storms can last. I know what it feels like when you think you can't get through it without the food or the diet. But giving in to the temptation is not worth it. I don't care how much your brain is telling you the sugar will help. It's temporary. Nothing compares to the strength you get by clinging to Christ when those cravings come. Yes, I know those times where it just feels like one thing after another. You are burned out. You just want to give up. But you don't. You know why? Because we have a refuge. *"Taste an◆ see that the LORD is goo◆; blesse◆ is the one who takes refuge in him"* (Psalm 34:8). *"Go◆ is our refuge an◆ strength, an ever-present help in trouble"* (Psalm 46:1).

He is the only one who will satisfy our souls. I remember when I had surgery on my shoulder a few years ago. The doctor told me to be prepared for a yearlong recovery with physical therapy three times a week. There were times when I was so afraid of putting on weight that I wanted to just go on a diet. But the Lord just kept leading me back to the Word.

"An◆ so, ◆ear brothers an◆ sisters, I plea◆ with you to give your bo◆ies to Go◆ because of all he has ◆one for you. Let them be a living an◆ holy sacrifice—the kin◆ he will fin◆ acceptable. This is truly the way to worship him" (Romans 12:1 NLT). This isn't about showing off before and after pictures to get attention from others. This is about serving God with our bodies.

One of my favorite quotes is, "Don't tell God how big your storm is; tell the storm how big your God is" (unknown). There is also great Scripture for these times:

> *From the en◆s of the earth I call to you,*
> > *I call as my heart grows faint;*
> > *lea◆ me to the rock that is higher than I.* (Psalm 61:2)

I promise you, with God's help, you don't have to react to thoughts and emotions the way you always did in the past. This is where not having the substance or trigger foods in your body makes the biggest difference. By not escaping to the substance every time you feel, you practice how to be still no matter what they feel like and become stronger each time you face them. Just be patient with yourself as you navigate the stormy waters when they arise. Feelings are normal. They make you human. You are just learning to navigate life with them.

Will it will take time for your heart to build a new operating system? Yes. But God can and will help you with that. One of the best things you can do is to get into a habit of bringing your emotions to God every day. Writing them down helps you recognize them. Talk to your sponsor or mentor about them so another person knows. In recovery, this is part of the tenth step "Continued to take personal inventory and when we were wrong promptly admitted it."[14]

When those times come that you just want to pick up the food or go on the diet, here's a good thing to remember that recovering people often say: "There is nothing eating over this can do to make this any better." Remember how far you've come. Also, remember that you are not meant to live on bread alone. That hunger you think is physical is often actually spiritual. Nothing of the world can satisfy it the way God can. That's why Matthew 4:4 says, *"Jesus answere♦, 'It is written: "Man shall not live on brea♦ alone, but on every wor♦ that comes from the mouth of Go♦."'"*

Heavenly Father, only you know our hearts. You create♦ them. You know us better than we know ourselves. Lor♦, help us navigate those storm swells of emotions. Be our stea♦y force. Be our gui♦e. Remin♦ us you are there no matter what we feel. Reveal to us your presence when the waters are ♦eep. Teach us your ways as we navigate them with your help. Give us the ♦esire to seek you as our lighthouse in the storms. We love you, Lor♦, an♦ we know you love us. Be our strength when we are weak with emotions. Thank you, Lor♦. In Jesus's name. Amen.

Chapter 8

When It's Time to Address Your Mental Health

Genuine self-acceptance is not ◦erive◦ from the power of positive thinking, min◦ games or pop psychology. It is an act of faith in the Go◦ of grace.

—Brennan Manning

I know sometimes people like to sweep this one under the rug. It may seem easier to ignore mental health when you can't see it. You may think you can make it go away. But a lot of people can't. If that is you, this chapter is for you.

I know there are different ways to approach the treatment of mental health. Some address it through prayer and believe for God's healing. Others go to a doctor who works specifically on mental health, treating it just like a physical issue (which is what I do). Then, there are those who live with it and deny its existence. Whatever the case may be, if you have an inkling that you may need to address it, please don't let it go unchecked. You may think you are only hurting yourself because it's in your mind, but you greatly impact those around you whether you know it or not.

I know we live in a world that still attaches a stigma to treating mental health, even when you are courageous enough to address it. But we cannot afford to ignore the physiological makeup of our minds or try to treat mental health issues with behavior modification programs. Just like the rest of our bodies, our minds can get sick and affect our whole being. What's worse is the Enemy's favorite place to attack is our minds, and many people don't see it. Those negative thoughts you've been playing over in your mind for ages are not of God. They are from the Enemy. He hasn't just been attacking you where you are weak with food. He starts in your mind and attacks your thoughts. Every crippling fear you have, regret, shame, or belief that you have to lose the weight to live your life—it is all from the Enemy, even the belief that you need your comfort foods to get through everything. As I mentioned earlier, you've got to know your Enemy. "He was a murderer from the beginning, not holding to the truth, for there is no truth in him. When he lies, he speaks his native language, for he is a liar and the father of lies" (John 8:44).

Please do not take it lightly when I tell you the battle for your mind is a spiritual one. When you struggle with your thoughts, remember this:

> "For my thoughts are not your thoughts,
>   neither are your ways my ways,"
> declares the LORD.
> "As the heavens are higher than the earth,
>   so are my ways higher than your ways
>   and my thoughts than your thoughts." (Isaiah 55:8–9)

Your thoughts don't have to be the ultimate authority. God's are greater. That is comforting when you feel like your thoughts are running your life.

Another Scripture that has helped me in this area is, *"Do not conform to the pattern of this world, but be transformed by the renewing of your mind. Then you will be able to test and approve what God's will is—his good, pleasing and perfect will"* (Romans 12:2).

Don't let the world take hold of your mind. Let God transform it. Trust Him in things you try to figure out yourself.

Trust in the LORD with all your heart
*   an♦ lean not on your own un♦erstan♦ing;*
in all your ways submit to him,
*   an♦ he will make your paths straight.* (Proverbs 3:5–6)

The Bible will be your best resource for casting out the Enemy's lies. *"For the wor♦ of Go♦ is alive an♦ active. Sharper than any ♦ouble-e♦ge♦ swor♦, it penetrates even to ♦ivi♦ing soul an♦ spirit, joints an♦ marrow; it ju♦ges the thoughts an♦ attitu♦es of the heart"* (Hebrews 4:12). I also specifically recommend studying Ephesians 6 to learn about the armor of God. (I mentioned this earlier so it's pretty important.) There is a wonderful Bible study on this topic by author and Bible teacher Priscilla Shirer titled *The Armor of Go♦.* Another good read is *Battlefiel♦ of the Min♦: Winning the Battle in Your Min♦* by Joyce Meyer.

I will talk more in the next chapter about getting professional help. But before we go there, I just want to say one thing about the world of New Age spirituality. It is not from God. The way the world is today, there are many teachings and false prophets that will sound good natured, but they are like wolves in sheep's clothing. It is not the same kind of spirituality. If you want to seek God first, you will have to test the spirits, as Scripture says.

Dear frien♦s, ♦o not believe every spirit, but test the spirits to see whether they are from Go♦, because many false prophets have gone out into the worl♦. This is how you can recognize the Spirit of Go♦: Every spirit that acknowle♦ges that Jesus Christ has come in the flesh is from Go♦, but every spirit that ♦oes not acknowle♦ge Jesus is not from Go♦. This is the spirit of the antichrist, which you have hear♦ is coming an♦ even now is alrea♦y in the worl♦. (1 John 4:1–3)

If they aren't acknowledging Christ, they are not for you. Believe me I have been there. I read a lot of self-help and New Age books considered spiritual and self-help in my early recovery and in my life coach certification. I have even seen a few of the spiritual leaders speak live and witnessed the deception firsthand. Although many of them bring you to more self-awareness, the common factor is they don't point to God. It's either self or the universe. Let me tell you, in the times we live, it's not you or the universe that's going to carry you through the craziness. It's God.

I know this won't be the popular opinion with some of you, but I feel it's important to share my testimony on this. Don't let yourself end up on an endless search trying to find you when God is the one who can help the most. *"For whoever wants to save their life will lose it, but whoever loses their life for me an▸ for the gospel will save it"* (Mark 8:35).

You have to understand that if the devil is out to get you, you are in a spiritual battle. He will use anything to deceive you. *"But I am not surprise▸! Even Satan ▸isguises himself as an angel of light"* (2 Corinthians 11:14 NLT). It's not about what you think might be OK. It's about what's behind what you think is OK. The spiritual forces of darkness are very active these days. *"For our struggle is not against flesh an▸ bloo▸, but against the rulers, against the authorities, against the powers of this ▸ark worl▸ an▸ against the spiritual forces of evil in the heavenly realms"* (Ephesians 6:12). When you stay out of your obsession with food and diets, you are much more aware of it, which is another reason to stay in the Word and get in a supportive community where you can grow spiritually.

There is one more tool that might help you if you feel distant from God and aren't sure how to connect. In my first book, I referred often to listening for your "healthy voice." If you want to learn more about it, I recommend reading *Healthy Voice: Life Beyon▸ the Weight.* Essentially, it's a way to help you recognize God's voice over the lies of the Enemy. It helped me quite a bit, as well as many of my coaching clients.

Dear Lord, there are people reading this who have never acknowledged their mental health or even realized how much the Enemy attacks their minds. Father God, I just pray that you would give them the grace to do something about it with your help. Give them the desire to seek more of your Word to combat the Enemy's lies. Lord, help us to lovingly come alongside our friends and sisters who may struggle with this and give them our support. We know, Lord, you want us to have our minds set on you, so just give us the courage to do what we need to do to get there. In Jesus's name. Amen.

Chapter 9

When It's Time to Seek Professional Help

Instea• of your shame
you will receive a •ouble portion,
an• instea• of •isgrace
you will rejoice in your inheritance.
An• so you will inherit a •ouble portion in your lan•,
an• everlasting joy will be yours.

—Isaiah 61:7

For those of you who want to seek professional help, it can be hard to know where to start. The Enemy can use shame, fear, or the disapproval of loved ones to keep you from seeking it. If you know you need help, you've got to let these things go. I can tell you as someone who sought the help, I would not be the woman who loves the Lord the way I do today if I hadn't.

Some of us have been through traumatic experiences, often in early childhood that have affected the way we walk through life in a profound way. Those things have set off a virtual firestorm in our minds and bodies that have kept us reacting instead of responding to life. Our attachment to food and even diets has played a primary role in helping us cope. But there is a point where we don't need them anymore, and it's time to let them go. As we begin this chapter, I recommend praying for God to guide you to the right resources. Let Him steer the boat on this and help you make any decisions. I know that once I gave God the signal that I was ready, He laid out the path. I have no doubt He can do the same for you.

Before I started treatment at Milestones in Recovery on May 12, 2008, I had been in therapy before and previously diagnosed with generalized anxiety as well as panic disorder. Early treatment was with cognitive behavioral therapy (CBT). But I never discussed my issues with food or alcohol. It wasn't until I got into inpatient treatment that I was honest with myself enough to identify my addiction and start treating the root of the issue. That place was a gift from God because the team there helped me get out of the food, feel the feelings, and address the wounds in my heart. That is also where I started going to meetings. The whole experience really laid the foundation for the life I choose in recovery today. It certainly didn't fix me. But it helped me lay the groundwork for the continued work at home.

Recovery doesn't always come in the form of treatment. Whatever way you approach it, I recommend finding a psychiatrist (who is a licensed medical doctor) to diagnose your mental health situation, prescribe any medicine you might need to treat it, and then monitor it. But don't stop there.

You can't just leave it at medication because that can become a physical Band-Aid and even an escape for some. Do the talk therapy with a therapist or a Christian counselor to work through your issues. Your past traumas could be greatly affecting how you function today.

After treatment, my therapist did EMDR, which stands for eye movement desensitization and reprocessing. This was the most helpful kind of talk therapy for me because it allowed me to stop replaying old events in my mind that kept getting me mentally and emotionally stuck. "Eye Movement Desensitization and Reprocessing (EMDR) therapy is an extensively researched, effective psychotherapy method proven to help people recover from trauma and other distressing life experiences, including PTSD, anxiety, depression, and panic disorders."[15]

There is a wonderful book I recommend you read to help you better understand the science behind why this is more about what goes on in your brain than you realize: *Anatomy of a Food Addiction: The Brain Chemistry of Overeating* by Anne Katherine, MA. She talks about how a lot of it has to do with an imbalance in how your brain functions, specifically with the neurotransmitters serotonin and dopamine. I love what she says here:

> If you have a disorder in your serotonin functioning, you will experience metabolically caused cravings. You aren't morally weak or undisciplined; your body is screaming to you, "Eat! Eat!"
>
> What causes this? Perhaps you have fewer serotonin neurons than most people. Perhaps this condition was inherited. . . .
>
> Whatever the cause, chemically caused eating is not your fault. You don't cause it. You're not bad for having this problem. It's a physical abnormality like diabetes.
>
> The problem is chemically based, and you can do something about it. You aren't helpless![16]

Guess what else? You don't have to be scared of a diagnosis. Getting one will tell you where you do indeed have an imbalance and help you treat it like any other physical condition you might have. A lot of people would prefer not to be on medication, so they resist it. What I have learned from experience and have come to accept is that I can't go in and adjust my brain chemicals with my hands (or my willpower). Yes, there are things like exercise I can do to keep them in balance. But I still have an imbalance that is physiological. I've learned sometimes there aren't enough behavior changes you can make to compensate for that, and I'm OK with that. You have to find what works for you.

I know some of you may be reading this chapter with the hair on your arms standing up. I know not everyone has been through traumatic things and needs this. But it is crucial for some. If you are someone who doesn't, please do yourself a favor and support your sisters here that do seek it. Pray that they find the help they need and have compassion. You may not understand it. But think about where you struggle in life. You'd want them to have compassion for you. So judge less. Love more.

As far as those traumatic experiences, this is a heavy subject and therefore not something to be taken lightly. It is not uncommon for people to minimize or not recognize they've been through something. I know I used to think, "Oh, everyone's been through that. Who am I to get help for it if it's not a big deal?" The truth is that it was a big deal to you, and it greatly affected the way you live your life. It is your right to acknowledge the feelings. But it's also up to you not to stay there. Acknowledge it, feel what you need to do, and let it empower you to overcome it. Let God make you the victor over it instead of remaining the victim. Believe me, I didn't think my parents' divorce was anything. Then I started treatment, and it became the main thing I worked on for six weeks, which made me realize just how significant of an event it was.

I suggest taking a test called the ACES test, which stands for adverse childhood experiences.[17] This test is based on experiences you may have had from birth to seventeen. Many of them are linked to physical and mental health issues as well as addiction. That is another reason to address it because you want to be proactive about your future health. There is a wonderful book that helped me understand this better titled *The Body Keeps the Score: Brain, Mind, and Body in the Healing of Trauma* by Bessel van der Kolk, MD. It is science based, but I learned a lot about how I am and what I can do to get better because of that trauma.

I've shared multiple insights on what has helped me in this area that I hope are helpful. Just make sure you keep your mind set on God. He will put the professionals you need in your life to guide you. But He is your ultimate healer. These people are part of the road to deeper healing with Him.

One final note, this is a marathon, not a sprint. It has taken me many years, hard work in therapy, and being proactive about treating my mental health to get to where I am today. I know the Enemy wants my mind, so I stand ready. *"Be alert and of sober mind. Your enemy the devil prowls around like a roaring lion looking for someone to devour"* (1 Peter 5:8). Have courage. God has got you.

Lord God, I ask you to meet the person reading this right where they are. Give them the wisdom and the courage to receive this knowledge and do something about it. Prepare the people who will assist them when the time is right. Give them boldness as they discover what in the past may have been affecting their thoughts, behaviors, and health all these years. Wherever their hearts are broken, Lord, do what you do best and comfort them in those places. Remind them that no matter what happened, you are right there. Give them strength as they take steps forward. Thank you, Lord. In Jesus's name. Amen.

Chapter 10

Why the Deepest Healing Comes from God

There is no pit so ɑeep, that Goɑ's love is not ɑeeper still.
—Corrie ten Boom, Dutch writer

It's going to be hard to heal with God's help if you don't believe you are His. This is why the Word of God is so important. When we don't believe we are His, we doubt that He can heal us because of something in our past. We put our judgment of ourselves above who God says we are, which effectively puts us before God. But that thinking is, once again, the Enemy's strategy. You are a child of God, whether you believe it or not. All you have to do is look at Psalm 139:13: *"For you createɑ my inmost being; you knit me together in my mother's womb."* You were born with a purpose. First Peter 2:9 tells us, *"But you are a chosen people, a royal priesthooɑ, a holy nation, Goɑ's special possession, that you may ɑeclare the praises of him who calleɑ you out of ɑarkness into his wonɑerful light."*

It doesn't matter how deep that darkness you've dwelled in has been, the Lord wants to call you out of it into His light. This is why correcting your food and weight was never enough to reach those deep places where only God can go and truly heal you. It's one thing to heal your mind. It's another thing to heal your body. But it's a miraculous thing to let God heal your heart. This is where you finally begin to heal your heart wounds.

You can find comfort in the fact that there is no one on earth that knows you like He does. You can imagine there would be no better one to heal your wounds than the one who created you. Psalm 139 mentions this in verses 1–6:

You have searched me, LORD,
*   and you know me.*
You know when I sit and when I rise;
*   you perceive my thoughts from afar.*
You discern my going out and my lying down;
*   you are familiar with all my ways.*
Before a word is on my tongue
*   you, LORD, know it completely.*
You hem me in behind and before,
*   and you lay your hand upon me.*
Such knowledge is too wonderful for me,
*   too lofty for me to attain.*

Read that again. He knows everything about us, even the words about to come out of our mouths. There isn't enough knowledge to acquire on earth that can come close to what He knows. But we get to come to know Him and who He says we are. It is so much more richly rewarding than another weight-loss goal or food fix. The longer we stick to the surface repairs, the longer we deprive ourselves of God's deeper healing.

Does it take courage to let God heal your wounds? Yes, it does. The work of recovery and getting honest with yourself about where you've been mentally and emotionally is absolutely hard work. It is literally like training for one marathon after another but with your soul. I sometimes joke, but it feels pretty true, that when God has worked me through deep stuff to get healing, it's like I've had a spiritual workout for my soul. Letting God heal those heart wounds is deeply gratifying for your spirit and is so much better than satisfying the flesh. If you are walking this road, you are on the path to being an overcomer, a victor over what you've been through rather than the victim, and a spiritual warrior for the kingdom of God. This is no small feat. Give yourself credit for your courage.

Sometimes it helps to realize that this healing isn't something for you alone. It's actually part of God's greater plan to bring healing and redemption to our land, especially to those who've walked a similar journey. The world needs you to get better so you can be a light. I love this quote from Brennan Manning: "In a futile attempt to erase our past, we deprive the community of our healing gift. If we conceal our wounds out of fear and shame, our inner darkness can neither be illuminated nor become a light for others."[18]

If you love the darkness and stay stuck in the shame, the Enemy will try to keep you there and spread darkness. He doesn't deserve that power. Whatever you've been through, however the Enemy has tried to hold you back, God can still turn it around and use it for good.

Do you know the old saying, "Time heals all wounds"? Well, it's actually not true. Some people hold onto their wounds with the passage of time and never get healing. God will heal all wounds in His time and His way, if we let Him.

There is another saying, attributed to Akshay Dubey: "Healing doesn't mean the damage never existed. It means the damage no longer controls our lives." Sometimes there is fear around healing because you think you'll have to forgive and forget. The truth is you won't forget. But the healing will help you let go of the pain so you can stop drinking the poison of resentment and regret.

"He himself bore our sins" in his body on the cross, so that we might die to sins and live for righteousness; "by his wounds you have been healed." (1 Peter 2:24)

There are multiple examples in the Bible of Jesus's healing. There are multiple stories of women He healed. In Luke 8:40–56, He heals the woman who had been bleeding for twelve years when she touched the edge of His cloak. In verse 48 He said, "Daughter, your faith has healed you. Go in peace." Mary Magdalene, who was the first one to see Jesus when He rose from the dead, was said to have been healed of seven demons by Jesus in Mark 16:9. Then there was the Samaritan woman at Jacob's well in John 4:1–26. She thought because of her sin, she wasn't good enough to receive the gift of eternal life. But Jesus helped her address it and she received it. There are many stories of healing in the Gospels. Go find more of them. Healing wasn't just for that time. He still does it today.

> *Praise the Lord, my soul;*
>> *all my inmost being, praise his holy name.*
> *Praise the Lord, my soul,*
>> *an▸ forget not all his benefits—*
> *who forgives all your sins,*
>> *an▸ heals all your ▸iseases,*
> *who re▸eems your life from the pit*
>> *an▸ crowns you with love an▸ compassion,*
> *who satisfies your ▸esires with goo▸ things*
>> *so that your youth is renewe▸ like the eagle's.* (Psalm 103:1–5)

If you have come this far and you are committed, you are blessed. He's giving you wisdom and knowledge so you can release those shackles of sin. Just remember, God doesn't work on our time. He works in His time. Christine Caine says in her devotional *Unshakeable*: "Of course you want God to heal you quickly and painlessly. Like physical healing, though, the healing of your heart can take time. On top of that wisdom, remember this—healing can and does happen: your Great Physician is faithful and good."[19]

A few things important for you to know:

1. **God wants to heal your heart**. One of the best things you can do is to pray for Him to cleanse your heart.

Create in me a pure heart, O God,
*   and renew a steadfast spirit within me.*
Do not cast me from your presence
*   or take your Holy Spirit from me.*
Restore me to the joy of your salvation
*   and grant me a willing spirit, to sustain me.* (Psalm 51:10–12)

2. You can trust in His promises. *"I will sprinkle clean water on you, and you will be clean; I will cleanse you from all your impurities and from all your idols. I will give you a new heart and put a new spirit in you; I will remove from you your heart of stone and give you a heart of flesh. And I will put my Spirit in you and move you to follow my decrees and be careful to keep my laws"* (Ezekiel 36:25–27).

3. He can handle all of your baggage. *"For my yoke is easy and my burden is light"* (Matthew 11:30). Rest in Him. The verse just before this, Matthew 11:29 says, *"Take my yoke upon you and learn from me, for I am gentle and humble in heart, and you will find rest for your souls."* Lay your burdens down. Let Him heal your heart and do the spiritual surgery only He can do. Jeremiah 30:17 promises, *"But I will restore you to health and heal your wounds."*

4. Just stay willing and keep laying your heart wounds at His feet. Seek Him first instead of those escapes like dieting and overeating. Choose to learn the truth about who God says you are instead of ignoring it. *"You will seek me and find me when you seek me with all your heart"* (Jeremiah 29:13).

5. Know that God wants you to bear much fruit. *"You did not choose me, but I chose you and appointed you so that you might go and bear fruit—fruit that will last—and so that whatever you ask in my name the Father will give you"* (John 15:16).

6. He wants you to know just how much He loves you. *"This is love; not that we loved God, but that he loved us and sent his Son as an atoning sacrifice for our sins"* (1 John 4:10).

7. He wants you to know why He died on the cross for you and me.

But he was pierce• for our transgressions,
    he was crushe• for our iniquities;
the punishment that brought us peace was on him,
    an• by his woun•s we are heale•. (Isaiah 53:5)

Repeat this as an affirmation from God to yourself: "By his wounds I am healed." Also, pray:

Heal me, LORD, an• I will be heale•;
    save me an• I will be save•,
    for you are the one I praise. (Jeremiah 17:14)

These are all promises from the Bible that the Lord can heal you. Then let Him. I know it's scary stuff. I've been there. But remember:

Be strong an• courageous. Do not be afrai• or terrifie• because of them, for the LORD your Go• goes with you; he will never leave you nor forsake you. (Deuteronomy 31:6)

Lor• Go•, I know you want to heal the heart of whomever is rea•ing this. Give them the courage to stan• firm in the truth an• trust that you will bring them to a place of healing in your time. We know that it •oesn't always happen on this si•e of heaven. But we believe that you love us, that your plans are goo•, an• you will bring us through to victory over our heart woun•s. Thank you, Lor•, for your presence in our lives an• sacrifice on the cross. In Jesus's name. Amen.

Part IV

Making Recovery a Lifestyle

We have the idea that God is leading us toward a particular end or a desired goal, but He is not. The question of whether or not we arrive at a particular goal is of little importance, and reaching it becomes merely an episode along the way. What we see as only the process of reaching a particular end, God sees as the goal itself.

—Oswald Chambers

Chapter 11

Learning to Tune into God's Voice

Refuse to be content with just the knowledge of God, but insist on experiencing His presence.

—Kerri Weems

It is good to have goals. It is good to have a time picked out for when you want to complete a project. Signing up for road races is what made me run them. It was the commitment that made me have to train. But when you are following God, the purpose is to seek Him. There is no goal weight attached to His promises. He doesn't give us the road map. He just guides. That's exactly why we have to keep seeking Him.

Recovery is a lifestyle of seeking God's will for your life. Behavior change is a huge part of it. But the lifeline is connection to God. You've learned so far how important it is to keep your mind and body healthy in order to stay on the spiritual path. In doing so, you can truly live out what it says in Philippians 4:7. *"And the peace of God, which transcends all understanding, will guard your hearts and minds in Christ Jesus."*

But as the world shakes around us and the storms come and go in our lives, that continued connection to God is what will keep us on the path. Matthew 16:24–25 says, *"Then Jesus said to his disciples, 'Whoever wants to be my disciple must deny themselves and take up their cross and follow me. For whoever wants to save their life will lose it, but whoever loses their life for me will find it.'"* This is the absolute opposite of what the world teaches and is difficult to live out, but that's why you choose the lifestyle of recovery and continually seek Him.

For those of you who have been walking with the Lord for a long time, I pray you continue to do the work of Philippians 2:12–13 and *"continue to work out your salvation with fear an♦ trembling, for it is Go♦ who works in you to will an♦ to act in or♦er to fulfill his goo♦ purpose."*

Walking with God is a constant refining process. He is the one who prunes our branches so we can bear more fruit. John 15:1–2 says, *"I am the true vine, an♦ my Father is the gar♦ener. He cuts off every branch in me that bears no fruit, while every branch that ♦oes bear fruit he prunes so that it will be even more fruitful."* That's why Jesus says in John 15:4, *"Remain in me, as I also remain in you. No branch can bear fruit by itself; it must remain on the vine. Neither can you bear fruit unless you remain in me."*

When we make room for God, we learn how to remain in Him and see how He remains in us. You may not realize how much He is constantly speaking to you. You just have to take Him out of whatever box you've had Him in your whole life and let Him surprise you with His presence. You can even pray something like this, "Lord, help me to notice you working in my life. Reveal yourself to me in ways I can understand so that I can seek you more."

Let me give you some ways to recognize His voice.

A. Pray

Prayer is the portal that brings the power of heaven ♦own to earth. It is kryptonite to the enemy an♦ to all his ploys against you.

—Priscilla Shirer

Throughout this guide I have written prayers for you. They come when the Holy Spirit leads me, so I hope they have helped you get a sense of how to pray to God if it's intimidating.

If you feel like you don't know how to pray, don't overthink it. It's more about what's in your heart. Use whatever words you need to speak from that place. He's not looking for big words. God already knows your heart. He just wants to hear it from you. He wants you to be real about where you are so He can enter into that space with you.

It's also not about the list of things you want Him to do. It's actually more about listening for His guidance. It's about praying for His presence, peace, grace, mercy, and guidance while He works His will out in your life. Leonard Ravenhill said, "Prayer is not an argument with God to persuade him to move things our way, but an exercise by which we are enabled by his Spirit to move ourselves his way." It's also about knowing He can hear you. Too many people don't have enough of the truth to realize that God is listening. First John 5:14 says, *"This is the confi*ence we have in approaching Go*: that if we ask anything accor*ing to his will, he hears us."*

I know sometimes it doesn't feel like He answers prayers, but the truth is His will isn't to give us what we want, but to work out His will. There is always a bigger plan and there is often a lot of waiting. Just know He is there.

> *Wait for the LORD;*
>> *be strong an* take heart*
>> *an* wait for the LORD.* (Psalm 27:14)

The most important prayer is the one where you receive Jesus into your heart. When you recite it, it must come from your heart. It can't just be words. When you are ready, I pray you read this prayer out loud. It's called "The Sinner's Prayer."[20]

"Dear Lord Jesus, I know that I am a sinner, and I ask for Your forgiveness. I believe You died for my sins and rose from the dead. I turn from my sins and invite You to come into my heart and life. I want to trust and follow You as my Lord and Savior. In Your name, amen."

If you prayed this prayer, God bless you. Welcome to the family of God. If you aren't ready, that's OK. God will be there when you are ready.

B. Study Scripture

Stu•y this Book of Instruction continually. Me•itate on it •ay an• night so you will be sure to obey everything written in it. Only then will you prosper an• succee• in all you •o.
—Joshua 1:8 NLT

Studying the Bible isn't only about listening to a Sunday sermon on it or reading it on Instagram. It's about picking it up to study for yourself so you can live it out. Think of it like a love letter from God, rather than an old textbook. James 1:22 says, *"Do not merely listen to the wor•, an• so •eceive yourselves. Do what it says."* You can't do what it says if you don't read it with your own eyes.

Remember that it is *"alive an• active. Sharper than any •ouble-e•ge• swor•"* (Hebrews 4:12). There is nothing like it. No self-help book, no meditation app, and no positive words can come close to its power. It is the ultimate tool for healing your heart wounds. By reading it for yourself, you will get to know the Lord and defeat the lies of the Enemy that have consumed you for years. I know we live in a time when people say that Bibles are outdated and irrelevant. Nothing could be further from the truth. It's a lie from the Enemy who wants to remove it from the earth. But he can't. Defeat that lie by reading it for yourself.

If you need some help to get into it, you can get a devotional like *Jesus Calling* by Sarah Young that will guide you, has Scriptures to reflect on, and will get you daily in the Word. There are many options. You can get a Bible app to get into it too, but there is something about having your hands on the Bible itself.

The more you read it, the more it will seep like a healing balm into your mind. As far as where to start, you can begin wherever you want. Some people start from the beginning. Some start in the Gospels. I started in the New Testament because I needed that renewing-the-mind encouragement. Then I worked on the rest. I still read it as much as I possibly can and hopefully always will.

One more thing I want to mention is that there is a passage for any and everything you are going through in your life. There have been times I have been feeling something or going through something, and I just went to see what Scripture had to say about it, only to be blown away by a specific word the Lord gave me. It can guide you through anything.

C. Find a Church Family

The church is a hospital for sinners, not a museum for saints.
—Abigail Van Buren

The church isn't full of a bunch of perfect people, just as the Bible isn't full of them. If you go to a church where you feel like you can't bring your brokenness to the Lord and hear the Word adequately preached, then you may not be in the right church for you. You may need to shop around for one that is biblically based, where you feel the Holy Spirit alive among its members.

When you start to live out the Word, you need to surround yourself with people who are living that way too. People in recovery don't always understand that because not everyone there is reading the Word. We go to church to strengthen our relationship with God and connect with other believers. I also know that I play a role in walking with Christ. He saved me and leads me. But I must keep following Him. Finding a church home will help you feel more supported in your faith walk.

If you have been hurt by the people in a church you attended, ask the Lord to help you work through that. Humans are flawed. God is not. He can help you heal and find somewhere that speaks to how you connect to Him today. You can find a place where you feel connected to God, even if you didn't in the past. Pray for God to remove that block and help you forgive whoever hurt you so you can get the support you need.

I know when I started searching for the right church for me, it took me a while to let go of the thinking that God would be angry with me. Each time I went to the new church, I felt that guilt and fear a little less intensely. Eventually, I realized how much the Lord just loved that I wanted to seek out a relationship with Him, and I finally let go of what wasn't working. It was definitely a process. But I can tell you today I go to a church where I feel at home in Christ's body. I never thought I would say it, but I look forward to going every week and serving the people God has placed alongside me.

D. Listen to Christian Music

Only in the act of praise an∢ worship can a person learn to believe in the goo∢ness an∢ greatness of Go∢.

—C. S. Lewis

Just like there is always a Scripture that speaks to what you are going through, there is often a Christian song that does the same. So many times I've turned on a Christian radio station at just the right time when I needed to hear a specific song. Every time it happens, I think, "Wow, God, you knew. Thank you." This happens when I hear the song "Shoulders" by For King and Country. When the waves are big, that's one I turn to often.

I started tuning in one day when I was still in Washington DC, feeling really down on myself. I decided to set my alarm to the Christian radio station, which set in motion a lifting of my mood and a renewed sense of hope. Growing up, I thought the only songs about God were in a church hymnal. Many of them were so beautiful, they are imprinted on my mind. But I had no idea there was worship and Christian music that moved your soul the way some of it does.

That music is what I believe God used to draw me into a church that made sense for me. When you find a church that works for you, there is nothing like being able to worship God. To stand beside other believers in praise and thanksgiving, even in the storms, is a beautiful thing. Another incredible place to experience it is in a live-music venue. I've been going to see concerts since I was five years old, and I can tell you seeing these artists live is more powerful than any regular concert I've ever experienced. Take the opportunity if you have the chance.

If music is your language, it might be just the thing God uses to reach you. Never underestimate His abilities. Make sure your ears are open and your radio is tuned into it.

E. Spend Time in Nature

> For the LORD is the great God,
>> the great King above all gods.
> In his hand are the depths of the earth,
>> and the mountain peaks belong to him.
> The sea is his, for he made it,
>> and his hands formed the dry land.

> —Psalm 95:3–5

Do not underestimate how God uses nature to speak. Whether you are looking at a sunset in your own backyard or standing at the top of Grand Canyon National Park, He is there reminding you of His presence.

There are so many ways He speaks to us in nature. For me, sunsets are one of the biggest ways. To watch Him paint a sky is one of the most wonderful things in the world. Another favorite of mine is when the trees change color in the fall. It's such a beautiful reminder that seasons change, and He is with us through them all. I love to see the color of the water where we visit in Northern

Michigan. It's crystal blue. Sometimes you can see the rocks on the bottom. I could just stare at it for hours. Those are the things that stand out to me. What about you?

I also love taking walks in nature. It's a way to just tune into God by surrounding yourself with His glory. I love listening to worship music while I do it. It's like a walking prayer meditation. But you know what else? I love the simplicity of the birds. They truly do remind us of this Scripture: *"Look at the bir•s of the air; they •o not sow or reap or store away in barns, an• yet your heavenly Father fee•s them. Are you not much more valuable than they? Can any one of you by worrying a•• a single hour to your life?"* (Matthew 6:26–27).

What a fabulous way to see how simply God can teach us how much He loves us. I encourage you to walk out your door and be intentional about noticing how He shows up in nature.

F. Show Up and Give Back

You are the light of the worl•. A town built on a hill cannot be hi••en. Neither •o people light a lamp an• put it un•er a bowl. Instea• they put it on its stan•, an• it gives light to everyone in the house. In the same way, let your light shine before others, that they may see your goo• •ee•s an• glorify your Father in heaven.

—Matthew 5:14–16

Whatever you do, don't hide your light. When God brings you through the storm and helps you overcome this battle you've had with food and weight, please share what He has done with those who need it. You don't have to tell the whole world, but if God presents the opportunity to share it one-on-one, take it. In 12-step recovery the last step is devoted to this concept of carrying the message to others. There's even a saying, "You've got to give it away to keep it."

I do believe that God wants us to help each other get closer to Him. We aren't meant to get better just for ourselves. My husband always says, "You never know. What you might be going through, you may be going through for someone else,"—meaning there is someone who will go down the same road you did, see what God did in your life, and want what you have. Don't shy away from that. Let God use you. Also, don't think for a minute God only uses perfect people. He uses broken people who've been redeemed. *"But God chose the foolish things of the world to shame the wise; God chose the weak things of the world to shame the strong"* (1 Corinthians 1:27).

As I stated earlier, Rick Warren said, "Other people are going to find healing in your wounds. Your greatest life messages and your most effective ministry will come out of your deepest hurts." I hope this guide has helped you realize that being in community is a huge element of breaking the attachment to food and weight obsession.

If you go to 12-step meetings, keep going even when you feel better. People who aren't quite as far down the road as you need to hear from you. If you start going to church, you will meet other Christians who never imagined they could overcome what you have. Share your story. If you come across people in your everyday life who talk about this kind of struggle, you'll know you need to share because God has put these people in front of you and they need to hear your story.

Don't just get better for yourself. Get better so God can work through you to help someone else. Second Corinthians 1:3–4 says, *"Praise be to the God and Father of our Lord Jesus Christ, the Father of compassion and the God of all comfort, who comforts us in all our troubles, so that we can comfort those in any trouble with the comfort we ourselves receive from God."*

One other element of being in recovery from food issues is that you will likely lose weight. People will tell you that you look great and ask you how you did it. You will be a testament to God's grace and the program. Receive the compliment. But also, don't be afraid to tell them it wasn't another diet, it was God who finally helped you find something that worked for you. If they ask, you tell them more. If they don't like it, let it be. Just live the program. But, be bold in your faith. Give God the glory for helping you get out of your obsession with fixing your food and weight yourself. Don't limit yourself to before and after pictures. Tell people how God has transformed your heart beyond those. God's light will shine through you.

G. Rest in the Lord

> *Come to me, all you who are weary an◆ bur◆ene◆, an◆ I will give you rest. Take my yoke upon you an◆ learn from me, for I am gentle an◆ humble in heart, an◆ you will fin◆ rest for your souls. For my yoke is easy an◆ my bur◆en is light.*
>
> —Matthew 11:28–30

It's funny that rest would be the last part of this chapter because don't we all struggle with putting ourselves last when it comes to rest? But we have to make it a priority, and I'm not just talking about sleep. Yes, we should take self-care breaks. But we also have to experience real rest in the Lord Almighty and His mighty power. I have a friend who always reminds me of this Dallas Willard quote: "Ruthlessly eliminate hurry from your life." While the world worships busyness, we get this invitation to rest in the Lord: *"Be still an◆ know that I am Go◆"* (Psalm 46:10). I have this Scripture on my fireplace mantel so I can be constantly reminded of it.

Somehow you have to factor rest into your life, not just sitting down for a minute but spending time with the Lord. Also, you should be spending time doing fun things, relaxing things, and things to help you take it easy and appreciate life instead of racing through it. Resting helps you notice the gifts of God in your life.

Sometimes it's our souls that need a rest. Sometimes it's our minds that need a rest. Sometimes it's our bodies. Sometimes it's all of those. I love this quote from well-known pastor and author Joyce Meyer: "When your soul is resting, your emotions are okay, your mind is okay, and your will is at peace with God, not resisting what He's doing."[21] When we're rushing through life, we're absolutely resisting what He's doing because we think we're the ones who have the whole world in our hands. But we don't. He does. We need to rest and remember that we are human. We can't do everything. But . . . God.

> My flesh an◆ my heart may fail,
>> but Go◆ is the strength of my heart
>> an◆ my portion forever. (Psalm 73:26)

Here's another thing, if you don't slow down, your body will do it for you. I'm telling you this as someone who has had multiple orthopedic injuries, surgeries, and long recoveries from each. If you've ever had something like this happen that takes you out, you know you have no choice but to rest. I believe that is when the Lord says, "Are you ready now?" Every single time I've gone through one of those seasons, I have been brought to a deeper dependence on the Lord and realized truly that I can be still and know that HE is God, not me. Finally, don't forget that if God could rest in Genesis 2:2—"By the seventh ◆ay Go◆ ha◆ finishe◆ the work he ha◆ been ◆oing; so on the seventh ◆ay he reste◆ from all his work"—then you can rest too.

Chapter 12

Dealing with Triggers Beyond Food

*Be alert an• of sober min•. Your enemy the •evil prowls aroun•
like a roaring lion waiting for someone to •evour. Resist him,
stan•ing firm in the faith, because you know that the family
of believers throughout the worl• is un•ergoing the same kin•
of sufferings.*

—1 Peter 5:8–9

I have talked quite a bit about your trigger foods and how the
Enemy uses them to keep you weak. But I haven't talked as much
about some other sneaky things he uses as triggers. There's no
way I can cover all of them or know exactly what yours are, but I
wanted you to be conscious of a few of them.

What I'm talking about here are things like feelings, people,
places, and times in your life. That's why one of the greatest gifts of
recovery is to find out that you aren't just powerless over certain foods.
You are also powerless over people, places, and things. Some people
would say this is a terrible thing. I can tell you from years of experience that it is actually empowering. To know what you can control
and what you can't helps you let go of the stuff you can't change and
do something about the stuff you actually can. Don't get stuck thinking powerlessness is a weakness. It's more like a superpower.

As I talk about these, it may help you to envision this like a
game of Whac-A-Mole to make it a little more fun. Just like the
little moles that pop out of the holes when you play the game, these
triggers are going to pop up everywhere you go, and often when
you least expect it. They don't go away, so we have to be vigilant

because they are just tactics of the Enemy to distract you. Keep your focus on God, on remaining abstinent, on using your food plan, and the other resources I've shared here. Those things will strengthen you for when these unexpected things come your way.

A. Senses

You must learn to hee♦ your senses. Humans use but a tiny percentage of theirs. They barely look, they rarely listen, they never smell, an♦ they think that they can only experience feelings through their skin. But they talk, oh, ♦o they talk.

—Michael Scott

Our senses are a gift from God. They help us experience life more fully and be present in it. But we have to be careful about letting them guide us, especially if we have wrestled with food issues our whole life. Why? Because you and I both know how they can get us. All you have to do is drive by a Krispy Kreme and *see* the red light on to pull into the parking lot. Other times you can just see a picture of a pumpkin pie on your phone and think, "I have to have that now."

For others, all they may need to do is *smell* cookies baking at the grocery store and they can't resist the urge to put them in their carts. Some experts say that our sense of smell is the most powerful of our senses.

Or perhaps you are someone who only needs to *hear* a family member say, "Let's go get ice cream!" to give yourself permission to eat it.

Sometimes you only need to remember the *taste* of a food from your childhood to think you can't live without it because it's either tied to a good memory or brings back the idea of comfort.

Our senses are powerful, which is why we cannot let them run the show. I don't care how good these things smell, how good they look, or how good they sound—they aren't worth it. Just be aware of how your senses can try to work against you and make you eat something just because you *feel* like it.

For example, there are times when you visit someone that you haven't seen in ages and there is that one food you enjoyed together that you *feel* you must eat again in order to enjoy your time together. I can tell you that you'll actually be more in touch with each other and the memories if you feel instead of eat to bring them back.

When I visit my hometown, Philadelphia, my cravings could send me to a ton of places. One example is the convenience store Wawa. It has everything "Philly" you could want. I could easily go in there and buy multiple things to revisit my childhood. But I can appreciate the memories more without feeling physically worse by not getting those unhealthy foods. Be aware that when you *feel* like eating something, it's usually your feelings trying to run the show and the Enemy trying to throw you off track. The truth is when you have a food plan, you can make things that you want, when you want them, that will actually satisfy you.

B. The Big Storms of Life

A furious squall came up, and the waves broke over the boat, so that it was nearly swamped. Jesus was in the stern, sleeping on a cushion. The disciples woke him and said to him, "Teacher, don't you care if we drown?" He got up, rebuked the wind and said to the waves, "Quiet! Be still!" Then the wind died down and it was completely calm. He said to his disciples, "Why are you so afraid? Do you still have no faith?" They were terrified and asked each other, "Who is this? Even the wind and the waves obey him!"

—Mark 4:37–41

We talked earlier about these storms. But they can really trigger us, so I'm bringing them up again. Just like the disciples in the boat that day, we can all have trouble believing God won't let us drown. In the past we'd automatically turn to the foods that helped us numb ourselves. But we don't have to do that with God in our boat. The longer you remain in recovery and walk with the Lord, the more prepared you will be to face them.

Whether you just lost someone you love or you are trying to get through the day with your kids, a storm is a storm. How you respond emotionally to the storms is where you have to be vigilant. I'm not saying don't feel. I'm saying you don't have to escape with food in order to cope with those feelings.

> *Feelings are much like waves, we can't stop them from coming but we can choose which one to surf.*
> —attributed to Jonatan Mårtensson

Yes, sometimes these storms last longer than we want or expect. But that's why we just keep trusting God in the waiting. Even when we're angry, frustrated, exhausted, burned out, or overwhelmed, we have to remember He will carry us through.

Remember the Enemy wants to use the storms against you, but God wants to use them for good. *"You inten•e• to harm me, but Go• inten•e• it for goo• to accomplish what is now being •one, the saving of many lives"* (Genesis 50:20). Ride the waves and let the storm pass. Trust that God has a good plan for your life. *"For I know the plans I have for you,' •eclares the LORD, 'plans to prosper you an• not to harm you, plans to give you hope an• a future'"* (Jeremiah 29:11). We can forget this in those storms. We can think there is no way out of it. But . . . God. No matter how long those storms last for you, you are not alone in them.

Just remember that life happens in seasons. *"There is a time for everything, an• a season for every activity un•er the heavens"* (Ecclesiastes 3:1). Each season gives us its own storms to ride that can often be rough, but Psalm 34:18 tells us, *"The LORD is close to the brokenhearte• an• saves those who are crushe• in spirit."* You are not alone in these storms. You have the greatest captain anyone could have. Trust Him.

C. Times in Your Life

I just talked about navigating the emotions that come with the seasons of life. But there are also very specific times in our lives when we need to be aware of triggers. For example, for the ladies reading this, that time of the month may cause difficulties. Do you crave sweets or salt? Know what it is you automatically want and don't pick it up. You can get through these times of the month without picking up the trigger foods.

Maybe there are times of the week that are a trigger for you, like the weekends, when you get home, or late at night. Maybe there are times of the year such as fall or winter that make you crave those sweets. Or maybe it's something tougher like the anniversary of the loss of someone you loved. You just want to numb your feelings on that day. Be cognizant of where you are emotionally at those times. Instead of escaping with food, do something to remember your loved one that doesn't include food. Spend some quiet time with the Lord. Reach out to a friend in your support circle.

I mentioned earlier that there are times we can't function in the ways we normally would. We get injured, need surgery, or something else in our lives requires our attention. I know there was a season for me when I had my shoulder surgery. The doctor told me because of the complexity of the shoulder and how he was resetting it, it would take a year to recover, and it did. There were multiple times I was so uncomfortable, and that fear of gaining weight reared its ugly head. I did the opposite of what I wanted to do. I went deeper into Scripture instead of going on a diet. That's what we have to do when these times come in our life: resist the devil's temptations with the Word of God.

The other time of year like this is when you start thinking about being skinny. Commercials are everywhere. People are talking about it. Maybe it's the new year or the spring or the fall. Whatever season it is that you usually get tempted to go on a diet, remember you are on a path of trusting God for that, not yourself or your willpower alone.

D. People

Go♦ grant me the serenity to accept the things I cannot change, the courage to change the things I can, an♦ the wis♦om to know the ♦ifference.

—Reinhold Niebuhr

Whenever I get frustrated with people in my life, my husband says, "Meredith, you gotta expect people to be people." It seems so simple, but he's right. We should have realistic expectations when it comes to dealing with people because we are human too. The truth is the only person we can actually change is ourselves and our attitude. Maya Angelou said, "If you don't like something, change it. If you can't change it, change your attitude."

If you think you can control or fix others all the time, you'll always be stuck in someone else's lane, not your own. It's best to accept that people are going to trigger you. They are going to make you want to give up and make you want to eat or go on a diet. But you do not have to do that. You do not have to let the Enemy win. God has got you. If you find yourself getting frustrated, I recommend reading page 417 of *The Big Book*. "Acceptance is the answer to *all* my problems today. When I am disturbed, it is because I find some person, place, thing, or situation—some fact of my life— unacceptable to me, and I can find no serenity until I accept that person, place, thing, or situation as being exactly the way it is supposed to be at this moment. Nothing, absolutely nothing, happens in God's world by mistake."[22]

I am well aware this is not an easy concept. It's not a one-time thing. It's a process. When something is a process, you have to be in the moment. Sometimes in the program we say, "Trust the process," which alludes to trusting that God has you right where He wants you, and you can trust Him in the process. We also say, "Progress, not perfection," because if we stay on the journey and make progress, we will grow spiritually. We will never be perfect this side of heaven, but we can keep growing.

*Not that I have alrea*y obtaine* all this, or have alrea*y arrive*
at my goal, but I press on to take hol of that for which Christ*
Jesus took hol of me. Brothers an* sisters, I *o not consi*er*
myself yet to have taken hol of it. But one thing I *o: Forgetting*
what is behin an* straining towar* what is ahea*, I press on*
towar the goal to win the prize for which Go* has calle* me*
heavenwar in Christ Jesus.* (Philippians 3:12–14)

What is great about recovery and relationships is that their interaction truly teaches you to love and forgive. Scripture says, *"Love prospers when a fault is forgiven, but *welling on it separates close frien*s"* (Proverbs 17:9 NLT). With time, you can learn to accept others as they are, not how you would have them be. The beauty is that when you are not trying to control everyone else, you are free to work on your life. You can learn to separate yourself from another person's actions and emotions and set boundaries.

Dr. Henry Cloud, coauthor of the book *Boun*aries,* says, "One of the first signs that you're beginning to develop boundaries is a sense of resentment, frustration, or anger at the subtle and not-so-subtle violations in your life. Just as radar signals the approach of a foreign missile, your anger can alert you to boundary violations in your life."[23]

It is difficult to work on these. You will find that you are angry at yourself or someone else based on the boundaries you haven't had. But that's the place where growth begins. That's where that anger can empower you to actually start setting those boundaries.

That's also when you can bring your anger to God. First John 1:9 says, "If we confess our sins, he is faithful and just and will forgive us our sins and purify us from all unrighteousness." You can go to your sponsor to work through it emotionally and act it out in your everyday life. This is not a process you have to walk alone.

One of the most significant things I've learned about life is that the people with whom we struggle the most, teach us the greatest life lessons. You will always be presented with opportunities to learn to forgive and set boundaries. That is a blessing. Don't be surprised if you realize one day a resentment hasn't gone away. It may be coming up because the Lord wants you to have deeper healing. Remember what Jesus told Peter about forgiveness in Matthew 18:21–22: *"Then Peter came to Jesus an● aske●, 'Lor●, how many times shall I forgive my brother or sister who sins against me? Up to seven times?' Jesus answere●, 'I tell you, not seven times, but seventy-seven times.'"*

I have found in my recovery that the more I abstain from trigger foods or behaviors, the more I see how my lack of boundaries with trigger foods reflected my lack of boundaries in my relationships. Remember, when you start to get better, you will more than likely feel better about setting boundaries with people in your life because you are setting them first in the area you've had them the least.

For example, you expect your Aunt Sally to trigger you at Thanksgiving with a comment about your weight. Then she forces her desserts on you. If you have boundaries around food and weight, you will be able to shrug off whatever she says and say, "No, thank you," to her food because you already have boundaries.

The same thing goes for the next time you go out with that friend you usually binge eat with on the weekends. Instead of just giving in to all the temptation, you can place your order based on your food plan and abstain from the foods that trigger you. Your friend may not like it or think you are on a diet. But you will know what works for you and be able to set the boundary. That's why the food plan is so grounding, because it gives you boundary lines with food. It doesn't matter if someone doesn't like it because it's what works for you. Who knows? Your friend may see how peaceful you are around food and want what you have.

The most important thing to know when it comes to relationships is something I've had to learn myself: understand that life works in seasons. You need different people to walk with you through different seasons. Many of them will feel special to you, and you'll expect them to be in your life forever. They are special because they are a gift from God. But it's not for us to know how long we'll walk together. Only God knows. Rather than expecting relationships to never change, accept the fact that people are in your life for a reason, season, or a lifetime, and that is absolutely OK. You can trust God's plan and thank Him for putting them in your life when He did. Only God knows when they'll come into your life or how long they'll stay. Just trust that they are in your life for a reason, and He will show you the rest.

E. Places

There is a reason people in the program say that you have to change the people, places, and things in your life. That's because those are the things that can throw us off track. It's not just the act of not picking up trigger foods. It's not going to the places (or even the aisles) where we get them.

Now, I'm not saying don't go to grocery stores or eat out. I'm saying be conscious of the places you've gone to get your trigger foods and either avoid them or go somewhere else. It's like when an alcoholic stops drinking, they don't keep going to a bar or a liquor store. They even try different travel routes, so they don't have to drive by those places. They find other places to go, like a meeting.

Only you know what these might be for you. You are the one who will have to be honest with yourself, God, and your sponsor. Maybe it's the bakery at your grocery store or the cereal aisle or the pharmacy. Maybe it's the rest stop, the convenience store, or the fast-food place on your way home from work. Whatever it is, you are going to have to be proactive in your approach to these.

Some people don't have to avoid them and can just go in and make a different choice. Other people can't go anywhere near them. If you are in early recovery, I would be careful about how much you frequent those places as the temptations can be intense. As I said earlier, find different places to go. Maybe even have someone go with you or text your sponsor before you walk in the door if you have to go.

Since we live in such an online culture, I have to mention that world. The places you go online can affect your recovery. What comes across your screen and who you choose to follow can make or break you. What you feed your mind is important. When you go to places online, pray for God to guide you: "Father, lead me not into temptation."

Honestly, you may have to block or unfollow some people or organizations you may have been following. If they trigger you and make you want to eat or diet, that can be a red flag. I promise you that you won't miss out if you don't follow these pages. Remember, your recovery is a spiritual journey. You aren't focused on the weight this time. Don't follow those who make it all about food or weight loss. Don't follow those who make it solely about nutrition (unless you really like their recipes). Pages like these will want you to stay on the surface and avoid going deeper. God wants more for you than that. He wants to keep you close.

Let me just close this section of dealing with triggers with a prayer.

Father Go, *You know every tactic the Enemy uses in this rea*er's *life to* *istract them from focusing on you. Make them aware of these things that trigger them beyon* *foo* *an* *give them the courage to set boun*aries. *Give them the patience to persevere through the* *istractions they bring. Give them your strength in their weakness. In Jesus's name. Amen.*

Chapter 13

The Gift of Hindsight

*An• the Go• of all grace, who calle• you to his eternal glory in
Christ, after you have suffere• a little while, will himself restore
you an• make you strong, firm an• stea•fast.*

—1 Peter 5:10

Have you heard the saying, "Hindsight is 20/20"? Webster
defines *hin•sight* as "perception of the nature of an event after
it has happened." You get a different kind of hindsight in your
life when God is in it. When you see how much He's brought
you through or what He's healed you from because you walked
in obedience, you start to see His faithfulness. You start to see
how He really isn't going anywhere because He's been guiding
you the whole time.

There are things in my life that have just about broken me. I'm
sure you've had similar experiences.

When you start walking with God, you look back at the seasons in your life—the ones where you suffered, the ones where you
waited, the ones where you grieved, the ones where you thrived—
and you realize what a blessing it is to see how God works in your
life. You start to see how He really does work it all together for
good. Romans 8:28 says, *"An• we know that in all things Go• works
for the goo• of those who love him, who have been calle• accor•ing to
his purpose."*

Each time you look back and get that hindsight, you realize
He brought you through the fire once. He will do it again. Even
the way you were before you wanted that relationship with God,

when He seemed so far away, you realize He was actually close. You just had to get to the other side to see He was waiting for you.

I can remember a few very specific times in my life when God has done this.

The first time that comes to mind is losing my dad. It was one of those things I'd actually eat over as a kid because he left when I was young—I was terrified I'd lose him for good. Then I did. God took him in an instant. It was that event that made me feel even more surrendered to God because He was literally carrying me through it. It truly felt like the Lord comforted me with the words: "Let me be your Father in your dad's absence." What's even cooler is that almost a year to the day before this happened, I had gotten baptized in our church. God's timing sometimes blows my mind.

Another time was going through the multiyear process of infertility, waiting with expectant hope, and then being disappointed when we had to wait more or go down a different road. It felt like it was never going to end. At the beginning of that process, my husband and I made a commitment to God and to each other that we weren't going to force this. We would try some different ways to make this happen, but we trusted God's plan. We trusted Him for the outcome only He could give. Then He gave us a miracle in Ellie.

But you know what? Just a few months before she was conceived, we became pregnant out of nowhere. We thought, "Wow, OK. God, so this is your plan? We'll go with it." Then we had a miscarriage six weeks later, and the grief of that infertility journey felt worse than ever. But . . . God. By the end of that same year, we were pregnant again. I look back at that journey, and I truly believe if we had not had our hearts pointed toward God and, instead, made it all about what we wanted, we wouldn't be where we are today. That's the kind of hindsight you get with God. It doesn't mean you feel fabulous all the time. Being in the middle of a season and waiting is far from easy. But if you continuously trust Him in the midst of it, He will always bring you through it. Make sure, as you start walking with Him, that you look back at what He's done in your life. Remember what He is doing now because you are His chosen one. You are His child. You are loved more than any person on earth ever could love you by someone who died for you. He wants to make a way in your life.

So when you feel like you are stuck in the middle, maybe just wait. Trust that God will reveal more to you in the process. Remember what He's brought you through. You can even say, "God, I don't know what you are trying to teach me in this, but I'm listening." Praise Him for everything He has done, everything He is doing, and everything He will do in your life.

> Let all that I am praise the LORD;
>> with my whole heart, I will praise his holy name.
> Let all that I am praise the LORD;
>> may I never forget the good things he does for me.
> He forgives all my sins
>> and heals all my diseases.
> He redeems me from death
>> and crowns me with love and tender mercies.
>
> (Psalm 103:1–4 NLT)

Conclusion

The ⬩evil is vicious, but he's not victorious. An⬩ you, my frien⬩,
have everything you nee⬩ to ⬩efeat him.

—Lysa TerKeurst

Well, we have come to the end of this journey.

I'm so grateful you made it all the way through with me. I pray
this ending is but a beginning for you and maybe a new approach
to life. I hope God has touched your heart with His love and grace.
I hope He's brought you to a place of willingness that goes beyond
anything you've tried to change by yourself. I hope you've seen just
how much He wants to be your greatest strength in your weakness. I hope my words have been encouraging. More importantly,
I hope the Word of God I shared becomes imprinted on your heart
and gives you a desire to read more of it on your own.

My greatest hope is that this book has given you a desire to
walk more closely with God and maybe to find a relationship with
Jesus you never thought you could have. I pray God releases that
grip you've had on your willpower, your weight, and your food so
you can hold onto Him. I pray you have the desire to pick up the
tools I've presented here so God can do a work in you that you
never could yourself. Know that you are not alone. Many, many
more have gone ahead of you on this road, and many are walking
beside you. You've just got to look.

So let the Lord lead you. Let Him free your focus from food
and weight so you can be free to focus on Him. He has a much better life planned for you than you've thought. Don't put this book
on the bookshelf. Act on it. Make it come alive in your life. Use the

Bible like a sword for all the weapons the Enemy throws at you. Don't hide your light as it begins to shine brighter. Let God shine through you as you walk.

> *May God himself, the God of peace, sanctify you through and through. May your whole spirit, soul and body be kept blameless at the coming of our Lord Jesus Christ. The one who calls you is faithful, and he will do it.*
> —1 Thessalonians 5:23–24

Take care of yourself. May God be with you. May God heal you so you can be a vessel for His grace.

Acknowledgments

I am immensely grateful for the people God has put in my life to help make this book happen. Most of all, I have to thank the Lord for saving me from myself and for opening the door to victory in Him, so I could face the storms of life and have the strength to persevere. Thank you, Lord, for making me an overcomer in you. Thank you for giving me the inspiration, the gifting, and words to write this. I know it was all you. I pray it reaches just who you want it to reach.

To my husband, Mike, it's hard to put into words how grateful I am that God brought us together, but the fact that you support my work means more than you know. You are my rock, my team-mate, my best friend, my sounding board, and the best dad to your kids I could imagine. It's beautiful to watch, so thank you for being just the man God created you to be. To my Ellie, thank you for sacrificing the time you are too young to realize we're missing so Mommy could write this. I love you, sweet girl.

To the recovery community, there is no end to my gratitude for those who've walked before me and beside me to show me the way. A big thanks especially to Renee for being there.

For the writing team, Suzy Q, thanks for seeing the fire in me. Thanks to your team as well, for being patient with me while I took some time to have a baby. Especially to you Anita Agers-Brooks, you stuck with me and kept encouraging me. Thank you. An important note of thanksgiving to Dr. Marty Lerner. If it weren't for you making me get real from the very beginning of the recovery journey, I wouldn't be where I am. I'm forever grateful.

Finally, to my parents: Mom, thanks for just sticking with me while I figure all of this out. The seed of faith you planted in me as a kid has grown a little bigger and continues to grow. Thank you. I'm forever grateful. To Dad, man, I wish you were here to read this. But I know you are proud of me and always walk with me. I miss you every day. This one is for all those kids we talked about who shouldn't have to go through what we did thinking it was all about the diet for so long.

Notes

1. Rick Warren, *The Purpose-Driven Life: What on Earth Am I Here For?* (Grand Rapids: Zondervan, 2002), 275.

2. *Alcoholics Anonymous Big Book*, 4th ed. (New York: Alcoholics Anonymous World Services, 2002), 59.

3. *Alcoholics Anonymous Big Book*, 59.

4. *Alcoholics Anonymous Big Book*, 59.

5. "Abstinence and Recovery Policy Revised at WSBC 2021," Business Conference Policy Manual, 1988 [amended 2019, 2021], accessed September 9, 2021, https://oa.org/blog/news /abstinence-and-recovery-policy-revised-at-wsbc-2021/.

6. Mike Bickle and Dana Candler, *The Rewar•s of Fasting: Experiencing the Power an• Affections of Go•* (Kansas City: Forerunner, 2005), from the introduction.

7. Eleanor Roosevelt, *You Learn by Living: Eleven Keys for a More Fulfilling Life*, Fiftieth Anniversary Edition (New York: Harper & Row, 1960; repr., Harper Perennial, 2011), 29.

8. *Alcoholics Anonymous Big Book*, xxx.

9. Dr. Mark Hyman, "5 Clues You Are Addicted to Sugar," accessed September 9, 2021, https://drhyman.com/blog /2013/06/27/5-clues-you-are-addicted-to-sugar/.

10. "The Nutrition Source: Carbohydrates and Blood Sugar," Harvard T. H. Chan School of Public Health and Science, accessed July 18, 2021, https://www.hsph.harvard.edu/nutritionsource /carbohydrates/carbohydrates-and-blood-sugar/.

11. Sun Tzu, *The Art of War* (Minneapolis: Filiquarian, 2006), 7. This work is in the public domain.

12. *Alcoholics Anonymous Big Book*, 17.

13. *Alcoholics Anonymous Big Book*, 562.

14. *Alcoholics Anonymous Big Book*, 59.

15. "About EMDR Therapy," EMDR (Eye Movement Desensitization and Reprocessing) International Association (EMDRIA), accessed August 11, 2021, https://www.emdria .org/about-emdr-therapy/.

16. Anne Katherine, MA, "Chemical Warfare" in *Anatomy of a Foo♦ A♦♦iction: The Brain Chemistry of Overeating*, 3rd ed. (Carlsbad, CA: Gurze Books, 1991), 37.

17. "What ACEs/PCEs do you have?" Aces Too High, accessed September 15, 2021, https://acestoohigh.com/got -your-ace-score/.

18. Brennan Manning, *Abba's Chil♦: The Cry for the Heart for Intimate Belonging* (Colorado Springs: NavPress, 2015), 12.

19. Christine Caine, "Tough but Good: August 17," in *Unshakeable: 365 Devotions for Fin♦ing Unwavering Strength in Go♦'s Wor♦* (Grand Rapids: Zondervan, 2017), 242.

20. There have been many variations of this prayer over the years. This one is from Billy Graham, https://static.billygraham.org /sites/billygraham.org.uk/uploads/pro/2016/02/Wallet-Size StepstoPeacewithGod.pdf.

21. Joyce Meyer, "The Way to Give Your Soul a Vacation," *Christian Post*, October 31, 2010, https://www.christianpost.com /news/the-way-to-give-your-soul-a-vacation-47366/.

22. *Alcoholics Anonymous Big Book*, 417.

23. Henry Cloud and John Townsend, *Boun♦aries: When to Say Yes, How to Say No to Take Control of Your Life* (Grand Rapids: Zondervan, 1992), 277.

References

12-Step Recovery Programs
Consult these or do an online search for local resources.
- Alcoholics Anonymous—www.aa.org
- Overeaters Anonymous—www.oa.org
- OA: A Vision for You (OAV4U)
  —https://www.avision4you.info
- Food Addicts Anonymous (FAA)
  —https://www.foodaddictsanonymous.org
- Full of Faith Accountability (FOF)
  —http://www.fulloffaith.com/sponsorsaccountability.html
- Anorexics and Bulimics Anonymous (ABA)
  —https://aba12steps.org
- Celebrate Recovery—https://www.celebraterecovery.com
- Life Recovery Groups—https://liferecoverygroups.com

Books
- *Battlefield of the Mind: Winning the Battle in Your Mind* by Joyce Meyer
- *Healthy Voice: Life Beyond the Weight* by Meredith Terpeluk
- *Armor of God* Bible Study by Priscilla Shirer
- *The Body Keeps the Score: Brain, Mind, and Body in the Healing of Trauma* by Bessel van der Kolk, MD
- *Boundaries: When to Say Yes, When to Say No to Take Control of Your Life* by Dr. Henry Cloud and Dr. John Townsend
- *The Life Recovery Bible* (New Living Translation) from Tyndale House Publishers by Stephen Arterburn

<u>Other Resources</u>

- The Food Addiction Institute
  —https://www.foodaddictioninstitute.org
- The National Eating Disorders Association (NEDA)
  —https://www.nationaleatingdisorders.org
- Theresa Wright
  —https://sanefood.com/about/h-theresa-wright/
- Milestones in Recovery
  —https://www.milestonesprogram.org

Note: There are many nutritionists available. I suggest you find someone that understands OA recovery, treats food addiction, and uses a food plan. There are also many treatment centers available if you need one. I would suggest you look for one that has 12-step recovery to help you continue living in recovery when you leave.

About the Author

Meredith Terpeluk Schoeller is the author of *Healthy Voice: Life Beyon. the Weight*, a book about going beneath the surface instead of constantly focusing on weight. As a life coach, she has helped dozens of young women find a path out of eating disorders. She created a video-based behavior modification curriculum for Curves International and the Cleveland Clinic called *Curves Complete*. Previously, she worked in politics for President George W. Bush on his campaign and at the White House, as well as the Department of Health and Human Services. She holds two degrees from the University of Notre Dame.

Meredith lives a life in recovery. The most important thing to her is the relationship she's developed with God. Meredith resides in Southwest Michigan with her husband and daughter, Ellie. She enjoys going "Up North" and visiting with her twenty-something stepchildren. You can find her at www.meredithterpeluk.com.

Made in the USA
Coppell, TX
23 December 2024

43447941R00070